Principles of Neural Information Theory

Computational Neuroscience and

Metabolic Efficiency

James V Stone

Reviews of Principles of Neural Information Theory

This is a terrific book, which cannot fail to help any student who wants to understand precisely how energy and information constrain neural design. The tutorial approach adopted makes it more like a novel than a textbook. Consequently, both mathematically sophisticated readers and readers who prefer verbal explanations should be able to understand the material. Overall, Stone has managed to weave the disparate strands of neuroscience, psychophysics, and Shannon's theory of communication into a coherent account of neural information theory. I only wish I'd had this text as a student!

Peter Sterling, (co-author of *Principles of Neural Design*)
Professor of Neuroscience, University of Pennsylvania.

This excellent book provides an accessible introduction to an information theoretic perspective on how the brain works, and (more importantly) why it works that way. Using a wide range of examples, including both structural and functional aspects of brain organisation, Stone describes how simple optimisation principles derived from Shannon's information theory predict physiological parameters (e.g. axon diameter) with remarkable accuracy. These principles are distilled from original research papers, and the informal presentation style means that the book can be appreciated as an overview; but full mathematical details are also provided for dedicated readers. Stone has integrated results from a diverse range of experiments, and in so doing has produced an invaluable introduction to the nascent field of neural information theory.

Dr Robin Ince,
Institute of Neuroscience and Psychology, University of Glasgow, UK.

Essential reading for any student of the why of neural coding: why do neurons send signals they way they do? Stone's insightful, clear, and eminently readable synthesis of classic studies is a gateway to a rich, glorious literature on the brain. Student and professor alike will find much to spark their minds within. I shall be keeping this wonderful book close by, as a reminder to ask not just how brains work, but why.

Professor Mark Humphries,
School of Psychology, University of Nottingham, UK.

Title: Principles of Neural Information Theory
Computational Neuroscience and Metabolic Efficiency

Author: James V Stone

©2018 Sebtel Press

First Edition, 2018.
Typeset in LaTeX 2_ε.
First printing.

ISBN 978-0-9933679-2-2

Cover based on photograph of Purkinje cell from mouse cerebellum injected with Lucifer Yellow. Courtesy of National Center for Microscopy and Imaging Research, University of California.

For Fleur

I held you on my knee when you arrived
Held your hand as you slipped away.

Who would not weep to lose such a flower?
And if mere tears
Could rouse these petals from perfect sleep
You would be here already.

Contents

Preface

Who Should Read This Book? *Principles of Neural Information Theory* is intended for those who wish to understand how the fundamental ingredients of inert matter, energy and information have been forged by evolution to produce a particularly efficient computational machine: the brain. Understanding how the elements of this triumvirate are related demands knowledge from a range of academic disciplines but principally biology and mathematics. Accordingly, this book should be accessible to readers with a basic scientific education. However, it should also be comprehensible to any reader willing to undertake some serious background reading (see Further Reading). As Einstein said: *Most of the fundamental ideas of science are essentially simple, and may, as a rule, be expressed in a language comprehensible to everyone.*

General Principles. Some scientists consider the brain to be a collection of heuristics or 'hacks' accumulated over the course of evolution. Others think that the brain relies on a small number of general principles that underpin the diverse systems within it. This book provides a rigorous account of how Shannon's mathematical theory of information can be used to test one such principle, *metabolic efficiency*, with special reference to visual perception.

From Words to Mathematics. The methods used to explore metabolic efficiency lie in the realms of mathematical modelling. Mathematical models demand a precision unattainable with purely verbal accounts of brain function. With this precision comes an equally precise quantitative predictive power. In contrast, the predictions of purely verbal models can be vague, and this vagueness also makes them virtually indestructible, because predictive failures can often be explained away. No such luxury exists for mathematical models. In this respect, mathematical models are easy to test, and if they are weak models then they are easy to disprove. So, in the Darwinian world of mathematical modelling, survivors tend to be few, but those few tend to be supremely fit.

This is not to suggest that purely verbal models are always inferior. Such models are a necessary first step in understanding. But continually refining a verbal model into ever more rarefied forms is not scientific progress. Eventually, a purely verbal model should evolve to the point where it can be reformulated as a mathematical model, with predictions that can be tested against measurable physical quantities. Happily, most branches of neuroscience reached this state of scientific maturity some time ago.

Signposts. *Principles of Neural Information Theory* describes the raw science of neural information theory, unfettered by the conventions of standard textbooks. Accordingly, key concepts are introduced informally before being described mathematically.

Such an informal style can easily be misinterpreted as poor scholarship, because informal writing is often sloppy writing. But the way we write is usually only loosely related to the way we speak, when giving a lecture, for example. A good lecture includes many asides and hints about what is, and is not, important. In contrast, scientific writing is usually formal, bereft of signposts about where the main theoretical structures are to be found and how to avoid the many pitfalls which can mislead the unwary. So, unlike most textbooks, but like the best lectures, this book is intended to be both informal and rigorous, with prominent signposts as to where the main insights are to be found, and many warnings about where they are not.

Originality. The scientific evidence presented here is derived from research papers and books. Occasionally, facts are presented without evidence, either because they are reasonably self-evident or because they can be found in standard texts. Consequently, the reader may wonder if the ideas being presented were originated by the author. In such cases, be reassured that all of the material in this book is based on research by other scientists. Indeed, like many books, *Principles of Neural Information Theory* represents a synthesis of ideas from many sources, but the general approach is inspired principally by these texts: *Vision* (1981) [77] by Marr; *Spikes* (1997) [98] by Rieke, Warland, de

Ruyter van Steveninck, and Bialek; *Biophysics* (2012)[18] by Bialek; and *Principles of Neural Design* (2015)[114] by Sterling and Laughlin. Note that the tutorial material in Chapter 2 of this book is based on the author's book *Information Theory* (2015)[117].

In particular, Sterling and Laughlin pointed out that the amount of physiological data being published each year contributes to a growing *Data Mountain*, which far outstrips the ability of current theories to make sense of those data. Accordingly, whilst this account is not intended to be definitive, it is intended to provide another piton to those established by Sterling and Laughlin on Data Mountain.

Figures. Graphs were either copied (with permission) from research documents, or were generated based on equations from those documents using MatLab. Figures not restricted by copyright can be downloaded: http://jim-stone.staff.shef.ac.uk/BookNeuralInfo/text/Figures.html

Corrections. Please email corrections to j.v.stone@sheffield.ac.uk. A list of corrections can be found at goo.gl/SYNheX

Acknowledgements. Thanks to Shashank Vatedka for checking the mathematics in a final draft of this book, and to Caroline Orr for copy-editing and proofreading. Thanks to John de Pledge, Royston Sellman, and Steve Snow for many discussions on the role of information in biology, to Patrick Keating for advice on the optics of photoreceptors, to Frederic Theunissen for advice on measuring neural information, to Karl Friston for discussing metabolic efficiency, and to Mike Land for help with disentangling neural superposition. Thanks also to Mikko Juusola and Simon Laughlin for discussions on information rates in the fly visual system, and to Mike DeWeese for advice on linear decodability. To Horace Barlow, thanks are due for lively debates on coding efficiency. For reading one or more chapters, I am indebted to David Attwell, Ilona Box, Julian Budd, Matthew Crosby, Hans van Hateren, Mark Humphries, Nikki Hunkin, Simon Laughlin, Raymond Lister, Danielle Matthews, Pasha Parpia, Anand Ramamoorthy, Jenny Read, Jung-Tsung Shen, Tom Stafford, Peter Sterling, Eleni Vasilaki, Paul Warren, and Stuart Wilson.

James V Stone, Sheffield, England, 2018.

To understand life, one has to understand not just the flow of energy, but also the flow of information.

William Bialek, 2012.

Chapter 1

In the Light of Evolution

When we see, we are not interpreting the pattern of light intensity that falls on our retina; we are interpreting the pattern of spikes that the million cells of our optic nerve send to the brain.
Rieke, Warland, de Ruyter van Steveninck, and Bialek, 1997.

1.1. Introduction

Just as a bird cannot fly without obeying the laws of physics, so a brain cannot function without obeying the laws of information. And, just as the shape of a bird's wing is determined by the laws of physics, so the structure of a neuron is determined by the laws of information.

Neurons communicate information, and that is pretty much all that they do. But neurons are extraordinarily expensive to make, maintain, and use[67]. Half of a child's energy budget, and a fifth of an adult's budget, is required just to keep the brain ticking over[110] (Figure 1.1). For both children and adults, half the brain's energy budget is used for neuronal information processing, and the rest is used for basic maintenance[9]. The high cost of using neurons accounts for the fact that only 2–4% of them are active at any one time[69]. Given that neurons are so expensive, we should be unsurprised to find that they have evolved to process information efficiently.

1

1.2. All That We See

All that we see begins with an image formed on the eye's *retina* (Figure 1.2). Initially, this image is recorded by 126 million photoreceptors within the retina. The outputs of these photoreceptors are then repackaged or *encoded*, via a series of intermediate connections, into a sequence of digital pulses or *spikes* that travel through the one million *neurons* of the *optic nerve* which connect the eye to the brain.

The fact that we see so well suggests that the retina must be extremely accurate when it encodes the image into spikes, and the brain must be equally accurate when it *decodes* those spikes into all that we see (Figure 1.3). But the eye and brain are not only good at translating the world into spikes, and spikes into perception: they are also efficient at transmitting information from the eye to the brain. Precisely how efficient is the subject of this book.

1.3. In the Light of Evolution

In 1973, the evolutionary biologist Dobzhansky famously wrote: *Nothing in biology makes sense except in the light of evolution.* But evolution has to operate within limits set by the laws of physics and (as we shall see) the laws of information.

In the context of the Darwin–Wallace theory of evolution, it seems self-evident that neurons should be efficient. But, in order to formalise

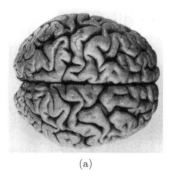
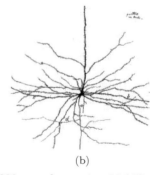

(a)   (b)

Figure 1.1. (a) The human brain weighs 1300 g, and contains 86 billion neurons. The outer surface seen here is the *neocortex*. (b) A neocortical neuron. From Wikimedia Commons.

the notion of efficiency, we need a rigorous definition of Darwinian fitness. Even though fitness can be measured in terms of the number of offspring an animal manages to raise to sexual maturity, the connection between neural computation and fitness is difficult to define. In the absence of such a definition, we consider quantities which can act as a plausible proxy for fitness. One such proxy, with a long track record in neuroscience, involves *information*, which is measured in units of *bits*.

The amount of information an animal can gather from its environment is related to fitness because information in the form of sight, sound, and scent ultimately provides food, mates, and shelter. However, information comes at a price, paid in neuronal infrastructure and energy. So animals want information, but they want that information at a price that will increase their fitness. This means that animals usually want *cheap* information.

It is often said that there is no such thing as a free lunch, which is as true in Nature as it is in New York. If an animal demands that a neuron delivers information at a high rate then the laws of information dictate that the price per bit will be high: a price that is paid in Joules. However, sometimes information is worth having even if it is expensive. For example, knowing how to throw a spear at a fast-moving animal depends on high-precision sensory-motor feedback, which requires neurons capable of processing large amounts of information rapidly. If these neurons take full advantage of their potential for transmitting information then they are said to have a high *coding efficiency* (even if the energy cost per bit is large). Conversely, if a task is not time-critical then each neuron can deliver information at a low rate. The laws of information dictate that if information rates

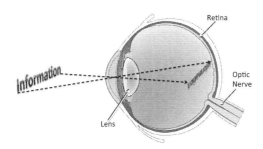

Figure 1.2. Cross-section of human eye. Modified from Wikimedia Commons.

are low then the cost per bit can be low, so low information rates can be achieved with high *metabolic efficiency*[70;114]. Both coding efficiency and metabolic efficiency are defined formally in Chapters 3 and 4.

The idea of coding efficiency has been enshrined as the *efficient coding hypothesis*. This hypothesis has been interpreted in a various ways, but, in essence, it assumes that neurons encode sensory data to transmit as much information as possible[87]. The efficient coding hypothesis has been championed over many years by Horace Barlow (1959)[14], amongst others (e.g. Attneave, 1954[8]; Atick, 1992[4]), and has had a substantial influence on computational neuroscience. However, accumulating evidence, summarised in this text, suggests that metabolic efficiency rather than coding efficiency may be the dominant influence on the evolution of neural systems.

We should note that there are a number of different computational models which collectively fall under the umbrella term 'efficient coding'. The results of applying the methods associated with these models tend to be similar[98] even though the methods are different. These methods include sparse coding[44], principal component analysis, independent component analysis[17;115], information maximisation (infomax)[71], redundancy reduction[6], and predictive coding[95;112].

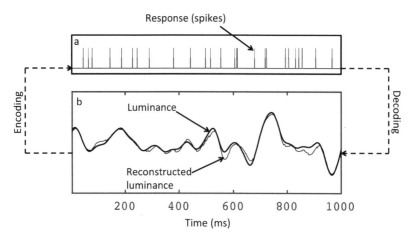

Figure 1.3. Encoding and decoding (schematic). A rapidly changing luminance (bold curve in b) is *encoded* as a *spike train* (a), which is *decoded* to estimate the luminance (thin curve in b).

1.4. In Search of General Principles

The test of a theory is not just whether it explains a body of data but also how complex the theory is in relation to the complexity of the data being explained. Clearly, if a theory is, in some sense, more convoluted than the phenomena it explains then it is not much of a theory. This is why we favour theories that account for a vast range of phenomena with the minimum of words or equations. A prime example of a parsimonious theory is Newton's theory of gravitation, which explains (amongst other things) how a ball falls to Earth, how atmospheric pressure varies with height above the Earth, and how the Earth orbits the Sun. In essence, we favour theories which rely on a *general principle* to explain a diverse range of physical phenomena.

However, even a theory based on general principles is of little use if it is too vague to be tested rigorously. Accordingly, if we want to understand how the brain works then we need more than a theory which is expressed in mere words. For example, if the theory of gravitation were stated only in words then we could say that each planet has an approximately circular orbit, but we would have to use many words to prove precisely *why* each orbit must be elliptical and to state exactly *how* elliptical each orbit is. In contrast, a few equations express these facts exactly, and without ambiguity. Thus, whereas words are required to provide theoretical context, mathematics imposes a degree of precision which is extremely difficult, if not impossible, to achieve with words alone. To quote Galileo Galilei (1564–1642):

> *The universe is written in this grand book, which stands continually open to our gaze, but it cannot be understood unless one first learns to comprehend the language in which it is written. It is written in the language of mathematics, without which it is humanly impossible to understand a single word of it.*

In the spirit of Galileo's recommendation, we begin with an introduction to the mathematics of information theory in Chapter 2.

1.5. Information Theory and Biology

Claude Shannon's theory of communication[105] (1948) heralded a transformation in our understanding of information. Before 1948, information was regarded as a kind of miasmic fluid. But afterwards, it became apparent that information is a well-defined and, above all, *measurable* quantity. Since that time, it has become increasingly apparent that information, and the energy cost of information, imposes fundamental limits on the form and function of biological mechanisms.

Shannon's theory provides a mathematical definition of information and describes precisely how much information can be communicated between different elements of a system. This may not sound like much, but Shannon's theory underpins our understanding of why there are definite limits to the rate at which information can be processed within *any* system, whether man-made or biological.

Information theory does not place any conditions on what type of mechanism processes information in order to achieve a given objective. In other words, information theory does not specify how any biological function, such as vision, is implemented, but it does set fundamental limits on what is achievable by any physical mechanisms within any visual system.

The distinction between a function and the mechanism which implements that function is a cornerstone of David Marr's (1982)[77] computational theory of vision. Marr stressed the need to consider physiological findings in the context of computational models, and his approach is epitomised in a single quote:

> *Trying to understand perception by studying only neurons is like trying to understand bird flight by studying only feathers: It just cannot be done.*

Even though Marr did not address the role of information theory directly, his analytic approach has served as a source of inspiration, not only for this book, but also for much of the progress made within computational neuroscience.

1.6. An Overview of Chapters

The following section contains technical terms which are explained fully in the relevant chapters and in the Glossary.

To fully appreciate the importance of information theory for neural computation, some familiarity with the basic elements of information theory is required; these elements are presented in Chapter 2 (which can be skipped on a first reading of the book). In Chapter 3, we use information theory to estimate the amount of information in the output of a spiking neuron and also to estimate how much of this information is related to the neuron's input (i.e. mutual information). This leads to an analysis of the nature of the neural code: specifically, whether it is a rate code or a spike timing code. We also consider how often a neuron should produce a spike so that each spike conveys as much information as possible, and we discover that the answer involves a vital property of efficient communication (namely, linear decodability).

In Chapter 4, we discover that one of the consequences of information theory (specifically, Shannon's noisy coding theorem) is that the cost of information rises inexorably and disproportionately with information rate. We consider empirical results which suggest that this steep rise accounts for physiological values of axon diameter, the distribution of axon diameters, mean firing rate, and synaptic conductance: values which appear to be 'tuned' to minimise the cost of information.

In Chapter 5, we consider how the correlations between the outputs of photoreceptors sensitive to similar colours threaten to reduce information rates, and how this can be ameliorated by synaptic preprocessing in the retina. This preprocessing makes efficient use of the available neuronal infrastructure to maximise information rates, which explains not only how, but also why, there is a red–green aftereffect but no red–blue aftereffect. A more formal account involves using principal component analysis to estimate the synaptic connections which maximise neuronal information throughput.

In Chapter 6, the lessons learned so far are applied to the problem of encoding time-varying visual inputs. We explore how a standard (LNP) neuron model can be used as a model of physiological neurons. We then introduce a model based on predictive coding, which yields similar results to the LNP model, and we consider how predictive coding represents a biologically plausible model of visual processing.

In Chapter 7, we consider how information theory predicts the receptive field structures of visually responsive neurons (e.g. retinal ganglion cells) across a range of luminance conditions. In particular, we explore how information theory and Fourier analysis can be used to predict receptive field structures in the context of van Hateren's model of visual processing. Evidence is presented to show that, under certain circumstances, these receptive field structures can also be obtained using predictive coding. We also explore how the size of receptive fields affects the amount of information they transmit, and the optimal size predicted by information theory is found to match that of physiological receptive fields.

Once colour and temporal and spatial structure have been encoded by a neuron, the resultant signals must pass through the neuron's nonlinear input/output (transfer) function. Accordingly, Chapter 8 explores the findings of a classic paper by Simon Laughlin (1981)[64], which predicts the precise form that this transfer function should adopt in order to maximise information throughput: a form which seems to match the transfer function found in visual neurons. In chapter 9, the main findings are summarised in terms of information theory.

A fundamental tenet of the computational approach adopted in this text is that, within each chapter, we explore particular neuronal mechanisms, how they work, and (most importantly) *why* they work in the way they do. Accordingly, each chapter evaluates evidence that the design of neural mechanisms is determined largely by the need to process information efficiently.

Chapter 2

Information Theory

A basic idea in information theory is that information can be treated very much like a physical quantity, such as mass or energy.
C Shannon, 1985.

2.1. Introduction

Every image formed on the retina and every sound that reaches the ear is sensory data, which contains information about some aspect of the world. The limits on an animal's ability to capture information from the environment depends on packaging (encoding) sensory data efficiently and extracting (decoding) that information. The efficiency of these encoding and decoding processes is dictated by a few fundamental *theorems*, which represent the foundations on which information theory is built. The theorems of information theory are so important that they deserve to be regarded as the *laws* of information[96;105;117].

The basic laws of information can be summarised as follows. For any communication channel (Figure 2.1): (1) there is a definite upper limit, the *channel capacity*, to the amount of information that can be communicated through that channel; (2) this limit shrinks as the amount of noise in the channel increases; and (3) this limit can very nearly be reached by judicious packaging, or encoding, of data.

2.2. Finding a Route, Bit by Bit

Information is usually measured in *bits*, and one bit of information allows you to choose between two equally probable, or *equiprobable*, alternatives. In order to understand why this is so, imagine you are standing at the fork in the road at point A in Figure 2.2, and that you want to get to the point marked D. The fork at A represents two equiprobable alternatives, so if I tell you to go left then you have received one bit of information. If we represent my instruction with a *binary digit* (0=left and 1=right) then this binary digit provides you with one bit of information which tells you which road to choose.

Now imagine that you come to another fork, at point B in Figure 2.2. Again, a binary digit (1=right) provides one bit of information, allowing you to choose the correct road, which leads to C. Note that C is one of four possible interim destinations that you could have reached after making two decisions. The two binary digits that allow you to make the correct decisions provided two bits of information, allowing you to choose from four (equiprobable) alternatives; 4 equals $2 \times 2 = 2^2$.

A third binary digit (1=right) provides you with one more bit of information, which allows you to again choose the correct road, leading to the point marked D. There are now eight roads you could have chosen from when you started at A, so three binary digits (which provide you with three bits of information) allow you to choose from eight equiprobable alternatives; 8 equals $2 \times 2 \times 2 = 2^3$.

We can restate this in more general terms if we use n to represent the number of forks and m to represent the number of final destinations. If you have come to n forks then you have effectively chosen from

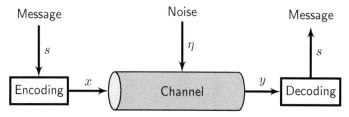

Figure 2.1. The communication channel. A message (data) is encoded before being used as input to a communication channel, which adds noise. The channel output is decoded by a receiver to recover the message.

$m = 2^n$ final destinations. Because the decision at each fork requires one bit of information, n forks require n bits of information.

Viewed from another perspective, if there are $m = 8$ possible destinations then the number of forks is $n = 3$, which is the *logarithm* of 8. Thus, $3 = \log_2 8$ is the number of forks implied by eight destinations. More generally, the logarithm of m is the power to which 2 must be raised in order to obtain m; that is, $m = 2^n$. Equivalently, given a number m which we wish to express as a logarithm, $n = \log_2 m$. The subscript $_2$ indicates that we are using logs to the base 2 (all logarithms in this book use base 2 unless stated otherwise).

Bits, Information and Binary Digits. The word *bit* is derived from *binary digit*, but they are fundamentally different types of quantities. A binary digit is the value of a binary variable, where this value can only be a 0 or a 1. In contrast, a bit is an *amount of information*, and the number of bits conveyed by a binary digit (when averaged over both of its states) can vary between zero and one. By analogy, just as a pint bottle can carry between zero and one pint of liquid, so a binary digit can convey between zero and one bit of information.

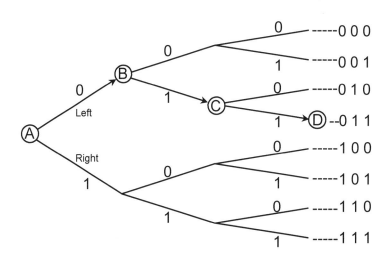

Figure 2.2. For a traveller who does not know the way, each fork in the road requires one bit of information to make a correct decision. The 0s and 1s on the right-hand side summarise the instructions needed to arrive at each destination; a left turn is indicated by a 0 and a right turn by a 1.

2.3. Information and Entropy

Consider a coin which lands heads up 90% of the time (i.e. $p(x_h)=0.9$). When this coin is flipped, we expect it to land heads up $(x=x_h)$, so when it does so we are less surprised than when it lands tails up $(x=x_t)$. The more improbable a particular outcome is, the more surprised we are to observe it. If we use logarithms to the base 2 then the Shannon information or *surprisal* of each outcome, such as a head x_h, is measured in bits (see Figure 2.3a):

$$\text{Shannon information} = \log\frac{1}{p(x_h)} \text{ bits}, \tag{2.1}$$

which is often expressed as: information $= -\log p(x_h)$ bits.

Entropy is Average Shannon Information. We can represent the outcome of a coin flip as the *random variable* x, such that a head is $x=x_h$ and a tail is $x=x_t$. In practice, we are not usually interested in the surprise of a particular value of a random variable, but we are interested in how much surprise, on average, is associated with the entire set of possible values. The average surprise of a variable x is defined by its *probability distribution* $p(x)=\{p(x_h),p(x_t)\}$ and is called the *entropy* of $p(x)$, represented as $H(x)$.

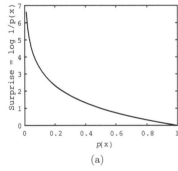
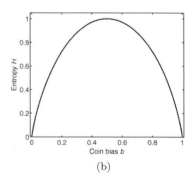

(a)   (b)

Figure 2.3. (a) Shannon information as surprise. Values of x that are less probable have larger values of surprise, defined as $\log_2(1/p(x))$ bits. (b) Graph of entropy $H(x)$ versus coin bias (probability $p(x_h)$ of a head). The entropy of a coin is the average amount of surprise or Shannon information in the distribution of possible outcomes (i.e. heads and tails).

The Entropy of a Fair Coin. The average amount of surprise about the possible outcomes of a coin flip can be found as follows. If a coin is fair or unbiased then $p(x_h) = p(x_t) = 0.5$; then the Shannon information gained when a head or a tail is observed is $\log 1/0.5 = 1$ bit, so the average Shannon information gained after each coin flip is also one bit. Because entropy is defined as average Shannon information, the entropy of a fair coin is $H(x) = 1$ bit.

The Entropy of an Unfair (Biased) Coin. If a coin is biased such that the probability of a head is $p(x_h) = 0.9$ then it is easy to predict the result of each coin flip (i.e. with 90% accuracy if we predict a head for each flip). If the outcome is a head then the amount of Shannon information gained is $\log(1/0.9) = 0.15$ bits. But if the outcome is a tail then the amount of Shannon information gained is $\log(1/0.1) = 3.32$ bits. Notice that more information is associated with the more surprising outcome. Given that the proportion of flips that yield a head is $p(x_h)$, and that the proportion of flips that yield a tail is $p(x_t)$ (where $p(x_h) + p(x_t) = 1$), the average surprise is

$$H(x) \quad = \quad p(x_h)\log\frac{1}{p(x_h)} + p(x_t)\log\frac{1}{p(x_t)}, \qquad (2.2)$$

which comes to $H(x) = 0.469$ bits, as in Figure 2.3b. If we define a tail as $x_1 = x_t$ and a head as $x_2 = x_h$ then Equation 2.2 can be written as

$$H(x) \quad = \quad \sum_{i=1}^{2} p(x_i) \log\frac{1}{p(x_i)} \text{bits}. \qquad (2.3)$$

More generally, a random variable x with a probability distribution $p(x) = \{p(x_1), ..., p(x_m)\}$ has an entropy of

$$H(x) \quad = \quad \sum_{i=1}^{m} p(x_i) \log\frac{1}{p(x_i)} \text{ bits}. \qquad (2.4)$$

This definition matters because Shannon's source coding theorem (see Section 2.5) guarantees that each value of the variable x can be represented with an average of (just over) $H(x)$ binary digits. However, if the values of consecutive values of a random variable are not independent then each value is more predictable, and therefore less surprising, which reduces the information-carrying capability (i.e. entropy) of the variable. This is why it is important to specify whether or not consecutive variable values are *independent*.

Interpreting Entropy. If $H(x) = 1$ bit then the variable x could be used to represent $m = 2^{H(x)}$ or two equiprobable values. Similarly, if $H(x) = 0.469$ bits then the variable x could be used to represent $m = 2^{0.469}$ or 1.38 equiprobable values; as if we had a die with 1.38 sides. At first sight, this seems like an odd statement. Nevertheless, translating entropy into an equivalent number of equiprobable values serves as an intuitive guide for the amount of information represented by a variable.

Dicing with Entropy. Throwing a pair of six-sided dice yields an *outcome* in the form of an ordered pair of numbers, and there are a total of 36 equiprobable outcomes, as shown in Table 2.1. If we define an *outcome value* as the sum of this pair of numbers then there are $m=11$ possible outcome values $A_x = \{2, 3, 4, 5, 6, 7, 8, 9, 10, 11, 12\}$, represented by the symbols $x_1, \ldots, x_{11}$. Dividing the frequency of each outcome value by 36 yields the probability P of each outcome value, as shown in Figure 2.4b and Table 2.1. Using Equation 2.4, we can use these 11 probabilities to find the entropy

$$H(x) = p(x_1)\log\frac{1}{p(x_1)} + p(x_2)\log\frac{1}{p(x_2)} + \cdots + p(x_{11})\log\frac{1}{p(x_{11})}$$

$$= 3.27 \text{ bits.}$$

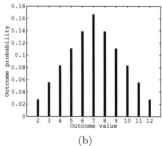

(a)   (b)

Figure 2.4. (a) A pair of dice. (b) Probability distribution (normalised histogram) of dice outcome values.

Using the interpretation described above, a variable with an entropy of 3.27 bits can represent $2^{3.27} = 9.65$ equiprobable values.

Entropy and Uncertainty. Entropy is a measure of *uncertainty*. When our uncertainty is reduced, we gain information, so information and entropy are two sides of the same coin. However, information has a rather subtle interpretation, which can easily lead to confusion.

Average information shares the same definition as entropy, but whether we call a given quantity information or entropy usually depends on whether it is being given to us or taken away. For example, if a variable has high entropy then our initial uncertainty about its value is large and is, by definition, exactly equal to its entropy. If we are told the value of that variable then, on average, we have been given an amount of information equal to the uncertainty (entropy) we initially had about its value. Thus, receiving an amount of information is equivalent to having exactly the same amount of entropy taken away.

2.4. Maximum Entropy Distributions

A distribution of values that has as much entropy (information) as theoretically possible is a *maximum entropy distribution*. Maximum entropy distributions are important because if we wish to use a variable

Symbol	Sum	Outcome	Frequency	P	Surprisal
x_1	2	1:1	1	0.03	5.17
x_2	3	1:2, 2:1	2	0.06	4.17
x_3	4	1:3, 3:1, 2:2	3	0.08	3.59
x_4	5	2:3, 3:2, 1:4, 4:1	4	0.11	3.17
x_5	6	2:4, 4:2, 1:5, 5:1, 3:3	5	0.14	2.85
x_6	7	3:4, 4:3, 2:5, 5:2, 1:6, 6:1	6	0.17	2.59
x_7	8	3:5, 5:3, 2:6, 6:2, 4:4	5	0.14	2.85
x_8	9	3:6, 6:3, 4:5, 5:4	4	0.11	3.17
x_9	10	4:6, 6:4, 5:5	3	0.08	3.59
x_{10}	11	5:6, 6:5	2	0.06	4.17
x_{11}	12	6:6	1	0.03	5.17

Table 2.1. A pair of dice has 36 possible outcomes.
Sum: outcome value, total number of dots for a given throw of the dice.
Outcome: ordered pair of dice numbers that could generate each symbol.
Freq: number of different outcomes that could generate each outcome value.
P: the probability that the pair of dice yields a given outcome value (freq/36).
Surprisal: $P\log(1/P)$ bits.

to transmit as much information as possible then we had better make sure it has maximum entropy (see Chapter 8). For a given variable, the precise form of its maximum entropy distribution depends on the constraints placed on the values of that variable[96]. It will prove useful to summarise three important maximum entropy distributions. These are listed in order of decreasing numbers of constraints below.

The Gaussian Distribution. If a variable x has a fixed *variance*, but is otherwise unconstrained, then the maximum entropy distribution is the Gaussian distribution (Figure 2.5a). This is particularly important in the context of metabolic efficiency because no other distribution can provide as much information at a lower energy cost per bit.

If a variable has a Gaussian or *normal* distribution then the probability of observing a particular value x is

$$p(x) \quad = \quad \frac{1}{\sqrt{2\pi v_x}} \, e^{-(\mu_x - x)^2/(2v_x)}, \tag{2.5}$$

where $e=2.7183$. This equation defines the bell-shaped curve in Figure 2.5a. The term μ_x is the mean of the variable x and defines the central value of the distribution; we assume that all variables have a mean of zero (unless stated otherwise). The term v_x is the variance of the variable x, which is the square of the standard deviation σ_x of x, and defines the width of the bell curve (see Appendix C). Equation 2.5 is a *probability density function*, and (strictly speaking) $p(x)$ is the *probability density* of x.

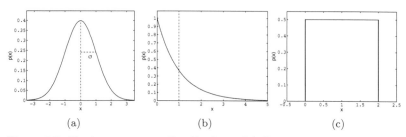

(a) (b) (c)

Figure 2.5. Maximum entropy distributions. (a) Gaussian distribution, with mean $\mu=0$ and a standard deviation $\sigma=1$ (Equation 2.5). (b) Exponential distribution, with mean indicated by the vertical line (Equation 2.6). (c) A uniform distribution with a range between zero and two (Equation 2.7).

In general, if values are drawn independently from a particular distribution then they are said to be *independent and identically distributed* (iid). If a variable x has values drawn independently from a Gaussian distribution $p(x)$ then it is *iid Gaussian*; and if it has a mean of μ_x and a variance of v_x then this is written as $x \sim \mathcal{N}(\mu_x, v_x)$.

The Exponential Distribution. If a variable has no values below zero and has a fixed mean μ, but is otherwise unconstrained, then the maximum entropy distribution is exponential:

$$p(x) \quad = \quad \frac{1}{\mu} e^{-x/\mu}, \tag{2.6}$$

which has a variance of $\text{var}(x) = \mu^2$, as shown in Figure 2.5b.

The Uniform Distribution. If a variable has a fixed lower bound x_{min} and upper bound x_{max}, but is otherwise unconstrained, then the maximum entropy distribution is uniform:

$$p(x) \quad = \quad 1/(x_{max} - x_{min}), \tag{2.7}$$

which has a variance $(x_{max} - x_{min})^2/12$, as shown in Figure 2.5c.

2.5. Channel Capacity

In the context of neural computation, a neuron is a *communication channel*, which has the key components shown in Figure 2.1. Our objective is to transmit a message reliably through the communication channel. The message or *source signal s* is essentially a physical quantity, such as a sound or a retinal image. The source signal is encoded using a function g to give the channel input $x = g(s)$. After the encoded message has been transmitted through the channel, the receiver observes the channel output y, which is a noisy version of x. However, consecutive values of natural signals are usually correlated, and neuronal channels are typically noisy, which reduces the rate at which information can be transmitted. In order to maximise information transmission, the signal s should be encoded into a form x in which consecutive values are independent, which helps to ensure that the channel is used efficiently.

A very important (and convenient) channel is the additive channel. As encoded values pass through an additive channel, noise η (eta) is added, so that the channel output is a noisy version y of $g(s)$:

$$y \;=\; g(s) + \eta. \tag{2.8}$$

The *channel capacity* C is the maximum amount of information that a channel can provide at its output about the input.

The rate at which information is transmitted through the channel depends on the entropies of three variables: (1) the entropy $H(x)$ of the input, (2) the entropy $H(y)$ of the output, and (3) the entropy $H(\eta)$ of the noise in the channel. If the output entropy is high then this provides a large potential for information transmission, and the extent to which this potential is realised depends on the input entropy and the level of noise. If the noise is low then the output entropy can be close to the channel capacity. However, channel capacity gets progressively smaller as the noise increases. Capacity is often expressed in bits per usage (i.e. bits per output). However, because we are interested in the *rate* at which information is transmitted through a neuron, we usually express capacity in bits per second (bits/s).

The Source Coding Theorem. Shannon's source coding theorem, described below, applies only to noiseless channels. This theorem is really about repackaging (encoding) data before it is transmitted, so that, when it is transmitted, every datum conveys as much information as possible. This theorem is highly relevant to the biological information processing because it defines definite limits to how efficiently sensory data can be repackaged. We consider the source coding theorem using binary digits below, but the logic of the argument applies equally well to any channel inputs.

Given that a binary digit can convey a maximum of one bit of information, a noiseless channel which communicates R binary digits per second can communicate information at the rate of up to R bits/s. Because the capacity C is the maximum rate at which it can communicate information from input to output, it follows that the capacity of a noiseless channel is numerically equal to the number R of binary digits communicated per second. However, if each binary digit carries less than one bit (e.g. if consecutive output values are correlated) then the channel communicates information at a lower rate $R < C$.

Consider a source which generates a stream of data in the form of signal values $s_1, s_2, \ldots,$ with an entropy of $H(s)$ bits per value, and a channel which transmits the corresponding encoded inputs $x_1, x_2, \ldots,$ where each input consists of C binary digits. *Shannon's source coding theorem* guarantees that if any source signal s has an entropy $H(s)$ then, when averaged over all values in s, (1) just over $H(s)$ binary digits are required to encode each value of s, and (2) each value of s cannot be encoded using any fewer than $H(s)$ binary digits. Recalling the example of the sum of two dice, a naive encoding would require 3.46 (log 11) binary digits to represent the sum of each throw. However, Shannon's source coding theorem guarantees that an encoding exists such that an average of (just over) 3.27 (i.e. log 9.65) binary digits per value of s will suffice (the phrase 'just over' is an informal interpretation of Shannon's more precise phrase 'arbitrarily close to').

This encoding process yields inputs with a specific distribution $p(x)$, where there are implicit constraints on the form of $p(x)$ (e.g. power constraints). The shape of the distribution $p(x)$ places an upper limit on the entropy $H(x)$ and therefore on the maximum information that each input can carry. Thus, the capacity of a noiseless channel is defined in terms of the particular distribution $p(x)$ which maximises the amount of information per input:

$$C \;=\; \max_{p(x)} H(x) \text{ bits per input.} \qquad (2.9)$$

This states that channel capacity C is achieved by the distribution $p(x)$ which makes $H(x)$ as large as possible (see Section 2.4).

Noise Reduces Channel Capacity. Here, we examine how noise effectively reduces the maximum information that a channel can communicate. If the number of equiprobable (signal) input states is m_x then the input entropy is

$$H(x) \;=\; \log m_x \text{ bits.} \qquad (2.10)$$

For example, suppose there are $m_x = 3$ equiprobable states, $x_1 = 100$, $x_2 = 200$ and $x_3 = 300$, so the input entropy is $H(x) = \log 3 = 1.58$ bits. And if there are $m_\eta = 2$ equiprobable values for the channel noise, say, $\eta_1 = 10$ and $\eta_2 = 20$, then the noise entropy is $H(\eta) = \log 2 = 1.00$ bit.

Now, if the input is $x_1 = 100$ then the output can be one of two equiprobable states, $y_1 = 100 + 10 = 110$ or $y_2 = 100 + 20 = 120$. And if the input is $x_2 = 200$ then the output can be either $y_3 = 210$ or $y_4 = 220$. Finally, if the input is $x_3 = 300$ then the output can be either $y_5 = 310$ or $y_6 = 320$. Thus, given three equiprobable input states and two equiprobable noise values, there are $m_y = 6 (= 3 \times 2)$ equiprobable output states. So the output entropy is $H(y) = \log 6 = 2.58$ bits. However, some of this entropy is due to noise, so not all of the output entropy comprises *information about the input*.

In general, the total number m_y of equiprobable output states is $m_y = m_x \times m_\eta$, from which it follows that the output entropy is

$$
\begin{aligned}
H(y) &= \log m_x + \log m_\eta & (2.11) \\
&= H(x) + H(\eta) \text{ bits.} & (2.12)
\end{aligned}
$$

Because we want to explore channel capacity in terms of channel noise, we will pretend to reverse the direction of data along the channel.

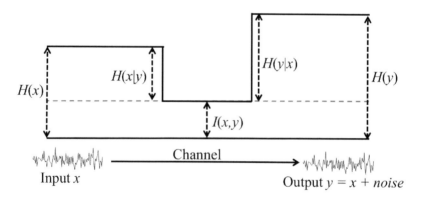

Figure 2.6. The relationships between information-theoretic quantities. Noise refers to noise η in the output, which induces uncertainty $H(y|x) = H(\eta)$ regarding the output given the input; this noise also induces uncertainty $H(x|y)$ regarding the input given the output. It can be seen that the mutual information is $I(x,y) = H(x) - H(x|y) = H(y) - H(y|x)$ bits.

Accordingly, before we 'receive' an input value, we know that the output can be one of six values, so our uncertainty about the input value is summarised by its entropy, $H(y)=2.58$ bits.

Conditional Entropy. Our average uncertainty about the output value given an input value is the *conditional entropy*, $H(y|x)$. The vertical bar denotes 'given that', so $H(y|x)$ is, 'the residual uncertainty (entropy) of y given that we know the value of x'.

After we have received an input value, our uncertainty about the output value is reduced from $H(y)=2.58$ bits to

$$H(y|x) \quad = \quad H(\eta) \quad = \quad \log 2 \quad = \quad 1 \text{ bit}. \tag{2.13}$$

Because $H(y|x)$ is the entropy of the channel noise η, we can write it as $H(\eta)$. Equation 2.13 is true for every input, and it is therefore true for the average input. Thus, for each input, we gain an average of

$$H(y) - H(\eta) \quad = \quad 2.58 - 1 \text{ bits} \tag{2.14}$$

about the output, which is the *mutual information* between x and y.

2.6. Mutual Information

The mutual information $I(x,y)$ between two variables, such as a channel input x and output y, is the average amount of information that each value of x provides about y:

$$I(x,y) \quad = \quad H(y) - H(\eta) \text{ bits}. \tag{2.15}$$

Somewhat counter-intuitively, the average amount of information gained about the output when an input value is received is the same as the average amount of information gained about the input when an output value is received, i.e. $I(x,y)=I(y,x)$. This is why it did not matter when we pretended to reverse the direction of data through the channel. These quantities are summarised in Figure 2.6.

The Noisy Channel Coding Theorem. Remarkable as it is, Shannon's source coding theorem ignores the effects of noise. In

21

contrast, an informal summary of Shannon's (equally remarkable) *noisy channel coding theorem* states that: *it is possible to use a noisy channel to communicate information almost without error at a rate arbitrarily close to the channel capacity of C bits/s, but it is not possible to communicate information at a rate greater than C bits/s.*

The capacity of a noisy channel is defined as

$$C = \max_{p(x)} I(x,y) \tag{2.16}$$

$$= \max_{p(x)} [H(y) - H(y|x)] \text{ bits.} \tag{2.17}$$

If there is no noise (i.e. if $H(y|x)=0$) then this reduces to Equation 2.9, which is the capacity of a noiseless channel. The *data processing inequality* states that, no matter how sophisticated any device is, the amount of information $I(x,y)$ in its output about its input cannot be greater than the amount of information $H(x)$ in the input.

2.7. The Gaussian Channel

If the noise values in a channel are drawn independently from a Gaussian distribution (i.e. $\eta \sim \mathcal{N}(\mu_\eta, v_\eta)$, as defined in Equation 2.5) then this defines a *Gaussian channel*.

Given that $y = x + \eta$, if we want $p(y)$ to be Gaussian then we should ensure that $p(x)$ and $p(\eta)$ are Gaussian, because the sum of two independent Gaussian variables is also Gaussian[96]. So $p(x)$ must be (iid) Gaussian in order to maximise $H(x)$, which maximises $H(y)$,

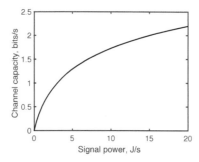

Figure 2.7. Gaussian channel capacity C (Equation 2.22) increases slowly with signal power S, which equals signal power here because $N=1$.

which maximises $I(x,y)$. Thus, if each input, output, and noise variable is (iid) Gaussian then the average amount of information communicated per output value is the channel capacity, so that $I(x,y)=C$ bits. This is an informal statement of *Shannon's continuous noisy channel coding theorem for Gaussian channels*. We can use this to express capacity in terms of the input, output, and noise.

If the channel input $x \sim \mathcal{N}(\mu_x, v_x)$ then the continuous analogue (integral) of Equation 2.4 yields the *differential entropy*

$$H(x) \quad = \quad (1/2)\log 2\pi e v_x \text{ bits.} \qquad (2.18)$$

The distinction between differential entropy effectively disappears when considering the difference between entropies, and we will therefore find that we can safely ignore this distinction here. Given that the channel noise is iid Gaussian, its entropy is

$$H(\eta) \quad = \quad (1/2)\log 2\pi e v_\eta \text{ bits.} \qquad (2.19)$$

Because the output is the sum $y=x + \eta$, it is also iid Gaussian with variance $v_y=v_x + v_\eta$, and its entropy is

$$H(y) \quad = \quad (1/2)\log 2\pi e(v_x + v_\eta) \text{ bits.} \qquad (2.20)$$

Substituting Equations 2.19 and 2.20 into Equation 2.15 yields

$$I(x,y) \quad = \quad \frac{1}{2}\log\left(1 + \frac{v_x}{v_\eta}\right) \text{ bits,} \qquad (2.21)$$

which allows us to choose one out of $m=2^I$ equiprobable values. For a Gaussian channel, $I(x,y)$ attains its maximal value of C bits.

The variance of any signal with a mean of zero is equal to its *power*, which is the rate at which energy is expended per second, and the physical unit of power is measured in *Joules* per second (J/s) or *Watts*, where 1 Watt = 1 J/s. Accordingly, the signal power is $S=v_x$ J/s, and the noise power is $N=v_\eta$ J/s. This yields Shannon's famous equation for the capacity of a Gaussian channel:

$$C = \frac{1}{2}\log\left(1 + \frac{S}{N}\right) \text{ bits,} \qquad (2.22)$$

where the ratio of variances S/N is the *signal-to-noise ratio* (SNR), as in Figure 2.7. It is worth noting that, given a Gaussian signal obscured by Gaussian noise, the probability of detecting the signal is [102]

$$P = \frac{1}{2}\log\left(1 + \text{erf}\left(\sqrt{\frac{S}{8N}}\right)\right), \qquad (2.23)$$

where erf is the *error function*.

2.8. Fourier Analysis

If a sinusoidal signal has a *period* of λ seconds then it has a frequency of $f = 1/\lambda$ periods per second, measured in *Hertz* (Hz). A sinusoid with a frequency of W Hz can be represented perfectly if its value is measured at the *Nyquist sample rate*[84] of $2W$ times per second. Indeed, *Fourier analysis* allows almost any signal x to be represented as a mixture of sinusoidal *Fourier components* $x(f)(f=0,\ldots,W)$, as shown in Figure 2.8. A signal which includes frequencies between 0 Hz and W Hz has a *bandwidth* of W Hz.

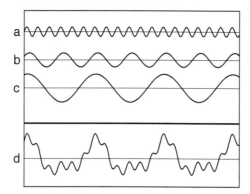

Figure 2.8. Fourier analysis decomposes the signal x in d into a unique set of sinusoidal *Fourier components* $x(f)$ $(f=0,\ldots,W\text{Hz})$ in a–c, where d=a+b+c.

Consider a signal y with a value y_t at time t, which spans a time interval of T seconds. This signal can be represented as a weighted average of sine and cosine functions,

$$y_t \;=\; y_0 \,+\, \sum_{n=1}^{\infty} a_n \cos(f_n t) \,+\, \sum_{n=1}^{\infty} b_n \sin(f_n t), \qquad (2.24)$$

where $f_n = 2\pi n/T$ represents frequency, a_n is the Fourier coefficient (amplitude) of a cosine with frequency f_n, b_n is the Fourier coefficient of a sine with frequency f_n, and y_0 represents the background amplitude (usually assumed to be zero).

The Fourier coefficients can be found from the integrals

$$a_n = \frac{2}{T} \int_0^T y_t \cos(f_n t)\, dt \quad \text{and} \quad b_n = \frac{2}{T} \int_0^T y_t \sin(f_n t)\, dt. \qquad (2.25)$$

Each coefficient a_n specifies how much of the signal y consists of a cosine at the frequency f_n, and b_n specifies how much consists of a sine. Each pair of coefficients specifies the power and *phase* of one frequency component; the power at frequency f_n is $S_f = (a_n^2 + b_n^2)$, and the phase is $\arctan(b_n/a_n)$. If y has a bandwidth of W Hz then its *power spectrum* is the set of W values $S_0,\dots,S_W$. Taken over all frequencies, these pairs of coefficients represent the *Fourier transform* of y.

An extremely useful property of Fourier analysis is that, when applied to *any* variable, the resultant Fourier components are mutually uncorrelated[98], and, when applied to any Gaussian variable, these Fourier components are also mutually independent (see Appendix C). This means that the entropy of any Gaussian variable can be estimated by adding up the entropies of its Fourier components, which can be used to estimate the mutual information between Gaussian variables.

Consider a variable $y = x + \eta$, which is the sum of a Gaussian signal x with variance S, and Gaussian noise with variance N. If the highest frequency in y is W Hz, and if values of x are transmitted at the Nyquist rate of $2W$ Hz, then the channel capacity is $2WC$, expressed as

$$C_{Rate} \;=\; W \log\left(1 + \frac{S}{N}\right) \text{ bits/s.} \qquad (2.26)$$

By convention, C represents both C_{Rate} (bits/s) and C (bits/value), as defined above; this notation will be adopted from now on. If the signal power of Fourier component $x(f)$ is $S(f)$ and the noise power of component $\eta(f)$ is $N(f)$ then the signal-to-noise ratio is $S(f)/N(f)$. The mutual information at frequency f is therefore

$$I(x(f),y(f)) \quad = \quad \log\left(1 + \frac{S(f)}{N(f)}\right) \text{ bits/s.} \qquad (2.27)$$

Because the Fourier components of any Gaussian variable are mutually independent, the mutual information between Gaussian variables can be obtained by summing $I(x(f),y(f))$ over frequency

$$I(x,y) \quad = \quad \int_{f=0}^{W} I(x(f),y(f)) \, df \quad \text{bits/s.} \qquad (2.28)$$

If each Gaussian variable x, y, and η is also iid then $I(x,y)=C$ bits/s, otherwise $I(x,y)<C$ bits/s [105]. If the peak power at all frequencies is a constant k then it can be shown that $I(x,y)$ is maximised when $S(f) + N(f)=k$, which defines a flat power spectrum (Section 7.7). Finally, if the signal spectrum is sculpted so that the signal plus noise spectrum is flat then the logarithmic relation in Equation 2.22 yields improved, albeit still diminishing, returns [98] $C \propto (S/N)^{1/3}$ bits/s.

2.9. Summary

We now have a mathematical definition of information, and we know how information is related to the distribution of signal values, sampling rates, and noise. Armed with this knowledge, we can begin to explore how the rate at which neurons communicate information is constrained by the availability of metabolic energy.

Chapter 3

Measuring Neural Information

Coding capacities are very large, close to the physical limits imposed by the spike train entropy.
Rieke, Warland, de Ruyter van Steveninck, and Bialek, 1997.

3.1. Introduction

The brain's fundamental processing unit is the neuron, first described by Ramón y Cajal in 1910, and illustrated in his beautiful drawings (see Figure 1.1b, which depicts a pyramidal cell in the cerebral motor cortex). In essence, each of the 86 billion neurons in the brain is a communication device, and what it communicates is information. Accordingly, our main task in this chapter is to explore the theoretical limits of neural information rates, in order to evaluate the performance of physiological neurons in the context of these theoretical limits.

3.2. The Neuron

A neuron is essentially an elongated tube of salty fluid, which acts a little like an electrical cable. It receives inputs via a bushy structure consisting of many filament-like structures or *dendrites*, which converge on the *cell body*. The neuron's output is delivered via a long cable-like structure called an *axon*, which is typically one micrometre (μm) in diameter (for comparison, a hair is $80\,\mu$m in diameter).

Each neuron has a membrane which is punctuated with tiny hatches or *ion channels*. The outside of the neuron is 70 millivolts (mV) higher than the inside, and this *resting potential* is represented with a minus sign (i.e. –70 mV). The ion channels in the membrane open and close according to the voltage across the membrane, and these are essential for the propagation of electrical signals through the neuron.

Spikes. Whilst the fundamental structural unit of the brain is the neuron, the currency of the brain is the *action potential* or *spike* (see Figure 3.1), which travels at *conduction velocities* between one metre per second and 120 metres per second (270 miles per hour). As the input to a neuron increases, a threshold is breached (at around –60 mV), which results in a rapid and transient decrease in the voltage across its membrane. This localised spike of decreased voltage opens a self-propagating bow-wave of voltage changes that travel along the neuron's axon: this is the action potential, which has an amplitude of 100 mV. If the input to a sensory neuron is increased by applying pressure to the skin, for example, then the number of action potentials per second, or *firing rate*, increases accordingly, as first discovered by Adrian (1926)[2]. The relationship between neuronal input and firing rate defines the neuron's input/output, or *transfer function*, which has a characteristic sigmoidal shape as shown in Figure 3.2. The transfer function corresponds to a *static nonlinearity* in signal processing[109].

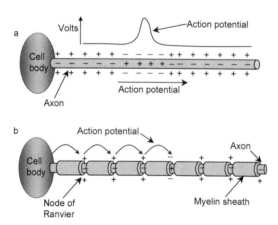

Figure 3.1. Action potentials or spikes. (a) The axon of an unmyelinated neuron actively propagates a spike along its length as a localised change in voltage. (b) In myelinated neurons, spikes 'jump' between gaps in the myelin sheath. Reproduced with permission from Stone (2012)[116].

Myelin Sheaths. Neurons that do not have a *myelin sheath* are like underground cables that lack insulation, so the transmission of signals is compromised as current leaks away into the surrounding tissue. In contrast, the addition of an insulating layer in the form of a myelin sheath effectively shelters the neuron, preventing its action potential from leaking away. However, even in an insulated cable a signal will eventually fade, so neurons have repeaters placed at regular intervals, each of which corresponds to a small gap, called a *node of Ranvier*, in the insulating sheath. Because the axon is insulated everywhere except at the nodes, each node allows ions to flood in and out as described above. Once an action potential is initiated at one node, passive conduction ensures the appearance of an action potential at the next node (see Figure 3.1b).

Synapses. Neurons communicate with each other across small gaps $(0.02\text{--}0.04\,\mu\text{m})$ called *synapses*. Data in the form of action potentials from many *presynaptic* neurons converge on the *cell body* of a single *postsynaptic* neuron where they release chemical *neurotransmitters*. Within the brain, the output of each neuron projects to more than 10,000 postsynaptic neurons.

Neurotransmitters diffuse across each synapse and bind to *receptors* on a postsynaptic neuron, which alters its membrane voltage. Neurotransmitters can be either excitatory or inhibitory. If enough excitatory neurotransmitters are released then a voltage *threshold* in the postsynaptic neuron is breached, and an action potential is initiated.

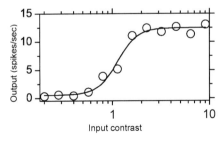

Figure 3.2. As the input to a neuron increases, its firing rate increases, which defines the neuron's input/output or *transfer function*. Reproduced with permission from Persi et al. (2011)[90].

3.3. Why Spikes?

The trouble with using continuously varying voltage values to transmit information is that they fade rapidly with distance and quickly become indistinguishable from background noise levels. This fading occurs because each successive length of axon decreases the voltage by a constant proportion. Consequently, the amplitude of a brief voltage pulse halves in value for each length of, say, $L_{50}=100\mu$m of axon, where L_{50} is the spatial analogue of a half-life. For example, if the initial amplitude is $V_0 = 100$ mV then it is $V_1 = V_0/2 = 50$ mV after $100\,\mu$m (i.e. after travelling for one half-length), $V_2 = V_1/2 = V_0/2^2 = 25$ mV after $200\,\mu$m (i.e. after two half-lengths), and so on. This means that the amplitude after travelling a distance L of n half-lengths is $V = V_0 2^{-n}$ mV, where $n = L/L_{50}\,\mu$m. This defines an *exponential decrease*, shown in Figure 3.3a, which is more usually defined in terms of a *space constant* λ_s:

$$ V \quad = \quad V_0\, e^{-L/\lambda_s}\ \text{mV}, \tag{3.1} $$

where λ_s is the distance over which voltage decreases by 67%.

The space constant is proportional to axon cross-sectional area, and is larger for myelinated than for unmyelinated axons[88] (because myelin reduces membrane capacitance). This means that the effective

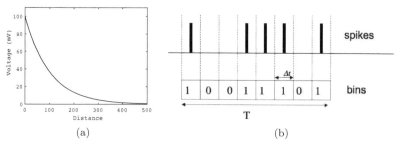

(a)   (b)

Figure 3.3. (a) Without active propagation in the form of an action potential, voltage decays exponentially with distance (μm) along an axon (Equation 3.1 with $V_0 = 100$ mV and $\lambda_s = 100\mu$m). (b) A sequence of n spikes can be represented as 0s and 1s. If a period of T seconds contains n spikes then the firing rate is $y = n/T$ spikes/s.

communication distance can be extended by increasing axon area. However, the metabolic cost of a neuron also increases roughly in proportion to its axon area. This implies that, given a desired output voltage, axon area must increase in proportion to axonal length. Thus, reliable communication beyond a certain axon length demands an axon area so large that it makes no sense to communicate using continuous voltage values. Typical space constants are $\lambda_s = 100$–$700\,\mu$m.

In contrast, because a spike is actively propagated, its amplitude does not decay with distance. Within the retina, neurons are only about $100\,\mu$m long, so a space constant of $\lambda_s = 100\mu$m is large enough to allow the use of continuous neuron voltages. In contrast, over the relatively long distance from the retina to the brain, neurons communicate using spikes. However, continuous voltage levels allow neurons to convey more than 2,000 bits/s, but once these voltages have been converted to spikes, this is reduced to 500 bits/s[114].

3.4. Neural Information

The first application of information theory to neuroscience was by MacKay and McCulloch[75] in 1952, a mere four years after the publication of Shannon's seminal paper[104]. The spirit of their approach has since been adopted and improved by others, and the following account is based on Rieke et al. (1997)[98].

The Information in Neuron Outputs. Our model of spike generation is based on the *Poisson process*. A fundamental assumption of a Poisson model is that spikes are mutually independent, so that the time at which each spike is generated is not affected by the time at which any other spike is generated.

Consider a reasonably long time period of T seconds, which has been divided into N small intervals Δt, where $N = T/\Delta t$, as in Figure 3.3b. It is assumed that Δt is sufficiently small that a maximum of one spike can occur in any time interval Δt and the maximum firing rate is $1/\Delta t$. For a given firing rate of y spikes per second (spikes/s), the probability that each interval Δt contains a spike is $P = y\Delta t$. The *expected* (i.e. average) number of intervals that contain a spike is $NP = Ny\Delta t$. However, if

T is made sufficiently long then the law of large numbers guarantees that the number of intervals that contain a spike is $n = NP$. Because spikes are assumed to be independent, each spike train that contains n spikes occurs with the same probability. In essence, given that all (long) spike trains generated by a firing rate y are equiprobable, the amount of information implicit in a spike train is just the logarithm of the number of different ways of arranging these n spikes amongst the N small intervals in that spike train. Our task is to estimate this number. However, in order to avoid the complicated mathematics that ends with a good approximation to the entropy of spike trains[98], we use less complicated mathematics to obtain a slightly less good approximation.

Given that the probability of a spike in each small interval is $P = y\Delta t$, the probability that no spike occurs in each interval is $Q = 1 - P$. By analogy with a coin which can yield a head with probability P or a tail with probability Q (Equation 2.2), this means that the average Shannon information of each interval Δt defines the output entropy

$$H \quad = \quad P\log(1/P) + Q\log(1/Q) \text{ bits.} \qquad (3.2)$$

In order to find the maximum *rate* at which information could be produced by a firing rate of y spikes/s, we divide by Δt, which defines

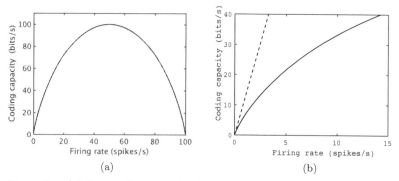

(a)   (b)

Figure 3.4. (a) How coding capacity R_{max} varies with firing rate y (Equation 3.3, $\Delta t = 0.01$s). (b) Close-up of (a), showing how R_{max} increases slowly with y. For comparison, a linear increase $y = R_{max}$ is shown as a dashed line.

the neural *coding capacity*[60]

$$R_{max} \quad = \quad H/\Delta t \text{ bits/s,} \tag{3.3}$$

as shown in Figure 3.4. The coding capacity is important because it defines an upper bound on output entropy and therefore on the amount of information that could be conveyed by a neuron. This means that it is impossible to use a firing rate of y spikes/s to transmit more than R_{max} bits/s. (Note that neural coding capacity refers to the maximum output entropy, whereas Shannon's channel capacity refers to the maximum mutual information between input and output.)

If we define Δt to be sufficiently small then the probability of a spike in each interval is also small, and therefore the probability of no spike is almost one, so that $Q \log (1/Q) \approx 0$ bits. Thus, the coding capacity defined in Equation 3.3 can be approximated by

$$R_{max} \quad \approx \quad \frac{P \log(1/P)}{\Delta t} \text{ bits/s,} \tag{3.4}$$

where $P = y\Delta t$, so that

$$R_{max} \quad \approx \quad y \log \frac{1}{y \, \Delta t} \text{ bits/s.} \tag{3.5}$$

Overall, Equation 3.5 implies diminishing returns on the extra information transmitted per second for each increment in the firing rate, as shown in Figure 3.4b. These diminishing returns mean that we should expect that the maximum information per spike (obtained by dividing coding capacity by firing rate) decreases with firing rate.

A neuron with a firing rate of $y = 15$ spikes/s with a timing interval of one millisecond ($\Delta t = 0.001$ s) has a coding capacity of $R_{max} \approx 15 \log 1/(15 \times 0.001) = 91$ bits/s. If 15 spikes convey 91 bits then each spike conveys an average of $91/15 \approx 6$ bits/spike. Notice that this is more than the information (one bit) conveyed by the state (spike or no-spike) of each bin, which can be understood if we adopt a slightly different perspective.

Given a firing rate of 15 spikes/s and a timing interval defined by 1,000 bins per second, an average of one bin out of every 67 bins

($\approx 1000/15$) contains a spike. Loosely speaking, this means that the *average set* of 67 bins contains one spike. Given that this spike can appear in any one of those 67 bins, the average set can adopt 67 equally probable states, so the average set has an entropy of $\log 67 \approx 6$ bits. And, because each average set contains one spike, each spike conveys an average of six bits of information. Thus, even though the state of a bin can provide one bit, the temporal precision defined by a particular bin width allows each spike to provide more than one bit.

If we assume that a neuron can fire at most once every Δt seconds then its maximum firing rate is $y_{max} = 1/\Delta t$ spikes/s. The firing rate which provides the maximum coding capacity[70;98] is $y = y_{max}/2$, as shown in Figure 3.4a (where $\Delta t = 0.01$ s). If $y = y_{max}/2$ spikes/s then the probability that each interval contains a spike is $P = 0.5$, which means that a maximum entropy (one bit) is associated with each interval.

3.5. Gaussian Firing Rates

It is common practice to assume that firing rates have a Gaussian distribution, which can be justified as follows. The probability $p(n)$ that n spikes occur in T seconds is given by the number N_{comb} of different spike trains which contain n spikes multiplied by the probability P_n that each spike train contains n spikes:

$$p(n) \quad = \quad N_{comb} P_n. \tag{3.6}$$

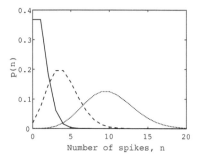

Figure 3.5. The number n of spikes in T seconds has a roughly Poisson distribution $p(n)$ (Equation 3.10). Each curve is a Poisson distribution with a different mean: $E[n] = \overline{y}T = 1$ (solid), $\overline{y}T = 4$ (dashed), $\overline{y}T = 10$ (dotted).

The values of $p(n)$ for different values of n define the *binomial distribution*, where N_{comb} is a *binomial coefficient*, which is the number of *combinations* of n identical items amongst N possible positions for each item. We can evaluate the terms N_{comb} and P_n as follows.

The number of different ways that n unique objects can be arranged in $N = T/\Delta t$ positions is $N_{perm} = N!/(N-n)!$, where each arrangement is a *permutation* and where $N! = N \times (N-1) \times (N-2)\ldots$. However, because one spike is very much like another, different permutations of n spikes amongst n positions are indistinguishable. In fact, the number of such permutations equals $n!$, so the number of different possible spike trains or *combinations* is

$$N_{comb} \quad = \quad \frac{N!}{n!(N-n)!}. \tag{3.7}$$

As an aside, this is part of the complicated analysis referred to in Section 3.4. Specifically, if all N_{comb} spike trains are equally probable then the spike train entropy is $\log N_{comb}$ bits, and the entropy rate is $(\log N_{comb})/T$ bits/s, which can be approximated[98] as

$$R_{max} \quad \approx \quad y \log \frac{e}{y \, \Delta t} \quad \text{bits/s}, \tag{3.8}$$

to which Equation 3.3 is a reasonable approximation.

Using the definitions of P and Q from Section 3.4, the probability that n intervals Δt contain a spike is P^n, and the probability that the remaining $N-n$ intervals do not is $Q^{(N-n)}$; and so the probability that n intervals contain a spike, and that $N-n$ intervals do not, is $P_n = P^n Q^{(N-n)}$. Therefore, Equation 3.6 yields

$$p(n) \quad = \quad \frac{N!}{n!(N-n)!} P^n Q^{(N-n)}. \tag{3.9}$$

If we increase N and T whilst keeping the average firing rate constant at $\overline{y}$ spikes/s then the distribution $p(n)$ of spike counts becomes an increasingly good approximation to a *Poisson distribution*

$$p(n) \quad = \quad \frac{(\overline{y}T)^n \, e^{-\overline{y}T}}{n!}, \tag{3.10}$$

which has a mean and variance of $\bar{y}T$ (see Figure 3.5). And if we set $T=1$ second then the firing rate is $y=n/T$ spikes/s, so $p(n)$ is identical to the distribution of firing rates $p(y)$.

More importantly, if the expected number of spikes observed in T seconds $E[n]=\bar{y}T=NP$ is large (e.g. if N is large and P is small) then this Poisson distribution is approximated by a Gaussian distribution (Figure 2.5b) with mean $\bar{y}$ and variance v:

$$p(y) \quad = \quad \frac{1}{\sqrt{2\pi v}}\, e^{-(y-\bar{y})^2/(2v)}, \qquad (3.11)$$

where $\bar{y}=NP/T$ and $v=\bar{y}(1-\bar{y}T)$. Indeed, the distribution $p(n)$ looks similar to a Gaussian distribution even for mean firing rates as low as $\bar{y}=10$ spikes/s, as shown in Figure 3.5. These numerical approximations agree with firing rates measured in neurons[33].

The Central Limit Theorem. The reason that $p(y)$ becomes increasingly Gaussian depends on the *central limit theorem*. As T is increased, the estimated firing rate becomes an increasingly good approximation to the overall mean firing rate. This implies that the firing rate measured within each interval is an increasingly good estimate of the overall mean firing rate, so that the distribution of measured firing rates is a distribution of mean firing rates. This allows us to invoke the central limit theorem, which guarantees that if T is sufficiently large (i.e. for large samples of firing rates) then the distribution of *mean* firing rates is approximately Gaussian, *almost irrespective of the distribution of firing rates* (see Glossary).

More generally, the central limit theorem states that, under fairly mild conditions, the mean of several independent variables is Gaussian, which allows us to assume that noise has a Gaussian distribution. This is because noise can be considered to be the sum of several independent physical processes, and because the distribution of sums is identical to the distribution of means, the distribution of noise values is Gaussian.

3.6. Information About What?

The fact that a neuron with a firing rate of 15 spikes/s can convey information at a maximum rate of $R_{max}=91$ bits/s is of little interest if these spikes supply almost no information or if almost none of the information supplied is *information about the neuron's input*. This under-utilisation of the available coding capacity can occur in two ways.

First, the output entropy R may be less than the coding capacity R_{max}. This can occur for two reasons: (a) because the distribution of outputs does not match the maximum entropy distribution for the channel under consideration; or (b) because consecutive neuronal outputs are not mutually independent. Koch et al. (2004)[59] report that the spike entropy R is about 85% of the neuronal coding capacity R_{max} in visual neurons, i.e. $R = 0.85 \times R_{max}$ bits/s. If we ignore (a), this suggests that 15% of coding capacity is lost due to correlations between outputs, although a later study[60] estimates this to be 9%.

Second, if only some of the entropy in the neuron's output is related to the neuron's input then the remainder is, by definition, noise entropy $H(\eta)$. The entropy in the neuron's output y that is related to its input x is the mutual information $I(x,y)$ between x and y (see Chapter 2); so the output entropy is $R = I(x,y) + H(\eta)$.

In practice, the mutual information $I(x,y)$ can be estimated using several methods[22] (see Appendix E). As their names suggest, the *lower bound method* provides a lower bound R_{min} on $I(x,y)$, and the *upper bound method* provides an upper bound[98] R_{info} on $I(x,y)$. Of course, the mutual information cannot exceed the output entropy R, and this in turn cannot exceed the neural coding capacity R_{max} (Equation 3.3).

We now have a hierarchy of estimates, as shown in Figure 3.6:

$$ R_{min} \ \leq \ I(x,y) \ \leq \ R_{info} \ \leq \ R \ \leq \ R_{max} \quad \text{bits/s.} \qquad (3.12) $$

Coding efficiency is a measure of the proportion of entropy in a neuron's output that comprises information about its inputs. However, in practice, we do not know the mutual information $I(x,y)$ or the entropy R exactly, so these are estimated as R_{info} and R_{max} respectively, which defines the coding efficiency[98]

$$ \epsilon \ = \ R_{info}/R_{max}. \qquad (3.13) $$

Testing for Coding Efficiency. Experiments by Rieke et al. (1997)[98] on the frog auditory system suggest that coding efficiency depends on the nature of the sounds used. Specifically, if artificial sounds are used then the coding efficiency is only about $\epsilon=0.20$, but if naturalistic frog calls are used then the coding efficiency is an impressive $\epsilon=0.90$. Additionally, Strong et al. (1998)[118] report that visually responsive (non-spiking) neurons in the fly typically have a coding efficiency of about $\epsilon=0.5$. More recent work[60] suggests that spiking neurons in the mammalian visual system have a coding efficiency of about $\epsilon=0.26$, a figure which is supported by other studies[88]. However, just because the output y of a neuron provides $I(x,y)$ bits about its input x, this does not imply that the brain can decode y to recover x.

Interpreting Neuronal Information Rates. Crickets have receptors sensitive to wind speed. Using data collected from these receptors, Warland found in 1992 (see Rieke et al., 1997[98]) that neurons have an entropy rate of about 600 bits/s. However, as noted above, about half of this entropy is related to the neuron's input, and the rest is noise. These neurons therefore transmit information about their inputs at a rate of about 300 bits/s.

Let's think about what it means for a neuron to provide 300 bits/s about its input. Using a simplistic interpretation, at the end of one second a neuron has provided 300 bits, which is enough information to specify its input to within one part in 2^{300} or (equivalently) as one part in 2×10^{90}. This would be analogous to measuring someone's height to within a fraction of the width of an atom, which is clearly silly.

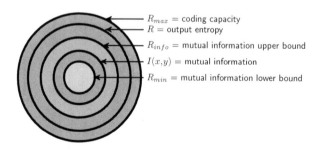

Figure 3.6. The components of neural coding capacity.

A more plausible interpretation, proposed by Rieke et al. (1997)[98], is that each neuron provides a 'running commentary' about its input. When considered like this, each neuron provides three bits each 10 ms. In other words, every 10 ms, a neuron's output specifies its input with a precision of one part in eight $(=2^3)$. For example, if a neuron is sensitive to wind speeds between zero and 32 cm/s then its output specifies one particular eighth of this range every 10 ms. Because $32/8 = 4$, the output now specifies a speed of, say, 20 ± 2 cm/s for the previous 10 ms.

3.7. Does Timing Precision Matter?

The timing interval Δt is a crucial quantity for analysing information in neurons, so we will take a few moments to consider its precise meaning. For this section only, we will distinguish between the *spike timing interval* Δt_g used by a neuron to generate spikes (defined as Δt above) and the *measurement timing interval* Δt_m used (by us or by another neuron) to measure spike timing. We then define *temporal precision* as $\iota = 1/\Delta t$ (ι is the Greek letter iota), the *spike timing precision* with which a neuron generates spikes as $\iota_g = 1/\Delta t_g$, and the *measurement timing precision* with which spike timing is measured as $\iota_m = 1/\Delta t_m$.

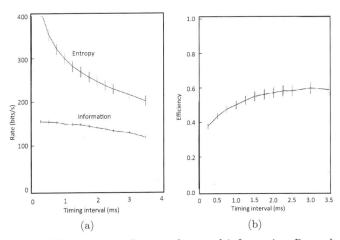

(a)   (b)

Figure 3.7. (a) How entropy R_{max} and mutual information R_{info} decrease with timing interval in cricket mechanoreceptors. (b) Coding efficiency (R_{info}/R_{max}) stays at about 50% over a large range of timing intervals (Δt). Reproduced with permission from Fred Rieke.

As Δt_m increases, so the amount of information obtained per second decreases. Thus, the more precisely spike timing is measured, the more information is gained, up to a limit defined by the spike timing precision ι_g. Specifically, we should expect the benefits of increased measurement precision to shrink as ι_m approaches ι_g and to vanish once $\iota_m < \iota_g$.

Using physiological data, both the estimated coding capacity and the mutual information of neurons fall as the measurement interval Δt_m increases, as shown in Figure 3.7a. Despite this, the coding efficiency remains fairly constant at about 50% (Figure 3.7b). However, DeWeese (1995)[36] reports a dramatic drop in mutual information (and therefore in coding efficiency) as the timing interval increases above a critical value Δt_c. Additional analyses[36] suggest that a coding efficiency of 50% is achieved if the mutual information conveyed by each spike is equal to a critical value of $I_c \approx 3$ bits. This is consistent with experimental results in Rieke et al. (1997)[98] and Harris et al. (2015)[50].

3.8. Rate Codes and Timing Codes

A question which frequently arises in the context of neural coding involves the distinction between *rate codes* and *spike timing codes*. If all of the information regarding inputs is implicit only in the firing rate of a neuron then the neural code is a rate code. However, different authors assume subtly different definitions for other types of code.

Each firing rate is consistent with many spike trains, so there are many more spike trains than there are firing rates (see Section 3.5). And, because information is the logarithm of the number of equally probable states, it makes sense to use a timing code. However, it is

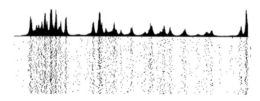

Figure 3.8. Spikes evoked from a visually responsive neuron (in area MT). Each dot represents a spike, and each row represents responses to a single presentation of the same 2-second movie. A histogram of spikes is plotted at the top of the figure. Reproduced with permission from Bair (1996)[11].

sometimes hard to distinguish between the two types of codes. For example, if n spikes occur in T seconds then the firing rate is $y=n/T$ spikes/s. But as T shrinks, the firing rate measures the timing of individual spikes, and therefore provides the same information as a spike timing code.

A striking indication of the fidelity of spike timing is given by Figure 3.8, which shows the response of a visually responsive neuron to repeated presentations of the same short movie[11;76]. The appearance of vertical stripes indicates that spikes occur at about the same time within each presentation, suggesting that the precise timing of spikes provides information. Indeed, Brenner et al. (2000)[26] compared the information rate of visual neurons in the fly when the interval between spikes is taken into account with the information rate when only the firing rate is considered; they found that information rates were almost twice as high when the timing between spikes is taken into account.

More recently, Jacobs et al. (2009)[54] measured the outputs of visually responsive retinal (ganglion) cells in a rat during a visual discrimination task in which each stimulus lasted for 300 ms. They compared the rat's performance to the performance of an *ideal observer model* using three different codes, namely: (1) a *rate code*, which makes use of only the mean firing rate; (2) a *spike timing code*, which uses the probability of a spike, given the state of the stimulus; and (3) a *correlation code*, which uses the probability of a spike and that a specified interval has elapsed since the previous spike, given the state of the stimulus. Compared to the rat's performance, the model performance based on (1) the rate code, (2) the spike timing code, and (3) the correlation code was considerably worse, slightly worse, and about the same, respectively. This does not imply that the rat uses a correlation code, because there are many other codes which could provide similar performance. But it does imply that the rate code (when measured over 300 ms) cannot be used for this task, because the performance of the ideal observer model with a rate code was worse than the rat's performance. However, beyond the eye, London et al. (2010)[74] report evidence that a rate code is used within the cortex.

Linear Decodability. Consider a time-varying stimulus which induces a series of spikes from a neuron. If the neuron's firing rate is high, relative to the rate at which the stimulus varies, then consecutive spikes contain information about related stimulus values. In this case, spikes are not independent, so the spike train cannot possibly achieve its coding capacity (Section 3.6). Conversely, if the firing rate is low then consecutive spikes contain information about unrelated stimulus values, so spikes are independent; but then spikes may be so infrequent that information about stimulus values at times between spikes is lost.

Clearly, the optimal firing rate lies between these two extremes and is related to the rate at which stimulus values change over time. This rate of change is defined in terms of the stimulus *correlation time* τ_c. Given stimulus values s_t and $s_{t+\tau}$ separated by an interval τ, the longer the interval, the more independent the values of s_t and $s_{t+\tau}$. Loosely speaking, the stimulus correlation time τ_c is the value of τ at which s_t and $s_{t+\tau}$ become independent of each other.

Crucially, if the firing rate y has a value such that a spike occurs once per correlation time (i.e. if $y\tau_c=1$) then the accuracy of stimulus values recovered from the spike train (Figure 1.3) using a linear filter cannot be improved by any nonlinear filter (Section 6.4). In practice, *linear decodability* is established by comparing the ability of linear and nonlinear filters to recover information. In essence, if a linear filter recovers as much information as a nonlinear filter then the spike train is linearly decodable. By making use of this logic, DeWeese (1995)[36] showed that spike trains are essentially linearly decodable. This, in turn, implies that neurons generate spikes roughly once per correlation time (see Bialek et al., 1993[19] and Rieke et al., 1997[98]), which also maximises the information gained per Joule (DeWeese and Bialek, 1995[37]). These observations are in agreement with recent analysis by Dettner et al. (2016)[35] and experiments by Brendel et al. (2017)[24].

3.9. Summary

Action potentials, or spikes, represent the primary currency for long-range communication in the brain. However, as we have seen, not all of the information in spikes refers to sensory data, because some of it is the result of noise.

Chapter 4

Pricing Neural Information

It appears likely that a major function of perceptual machinery is to strip away some of the redundancy of stimulation, to describe or encode incoming information in a form more economical than that in which it impinges on the receptors.

F Attneave, 1954.

4.1. Introduction

It is often said that there is no such thing as a free lunch, which is as true in Nature as it is in New York (as noted in Chapter 1). If a neuron delivers information at a high rate then the laws of information dictate that the metabolic cost per bit will be high. Conversely, if information is delivered at a low rate then those same laws dictate that the metabolic cost per bit can be low. These two scenarios seem to represent a trade-off between low metabolic efficiency (i.e. with high and expensive information rates) and high metabolic efficiency (i.e. with low and cheap information rates).

4.2. The Efficiency-Rate Trade-Off

In order to examine the nature of this trade-off uncluttered by the details of physiology, we begin with a straightforward example of an electrical signal in a Gaussian channel. If the signal power is S pico-Joules per second (pJ/s) and the noise power is N pJ/s then the information rate of a Gaussian channel is given by Equation 2.22 as $I = (1/2)\log(1 + S/N)$ bits/s. As was the case for neuron firing rates in the previous chapter, there are diminishing returns on power, as shown by the dashed curve in Figure 4.1a. Note that the variance of a zero-mean variable is proportional to power, and we choose to treat them interchangeably here. If the fixed cost of maintaining a channel is E_{rest} pJ/s then the total power required is $E=E_{rest}+S$ pJ/s. Thus, the amount of information obtained for each pico-Joule of energy expended is the *metabolic efficiency*

$$\varepsilon \;=\; I(x,y)/E \;\; \text{bits/pJ}. \tag{4.1}$$

The role of the baseline channel cost E_{rest} is crucial because it acts as a *constraint* on metabolic efficiency. Without this constraint, efficiency ε increases monotonically as E decreases, and it reaches its maximum value of $\varepsilon=\infty$ at $E=0$, but then the information rate I is zero, see Figure 4.1a. Of course, neurons have a non-zero baseline cost, so maximal metabolic efficiency is obtained at $I>0$ bits/s, as in Figure 4.1b.

Efficiency curves similar to the solid curve in Figure 4.1b are often observed when some quantity must be maximised under constraints imposed by a shortage of space, time, or energy. With regard to neural computation, we will see how such constraints may determine the values of physiological parameters like firing rate, axon diameter, and even receptive field size (Section 7.11). This type of problem has been analysed in the context of animal behaviour (e.g. *optimal foraging*

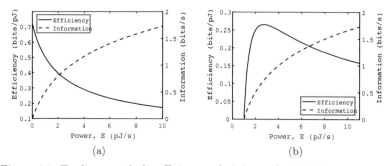

Figure 4.1. Trading metabolic efficiency ε (solid curve) with information rate I (dashed curve) in a Gaussian channel, with $N=1$. (a) If $E_{rest}=0$ pJ/s then efficiency peaks at $I=0$ bits/s. (b) If $E_{rest}>0$ pJ/s then efficiency peaks at $I>0$ bits/s ($E_{rest}=1$, here).

theory[32]), where it gave rise to the *marginal value theorem*[3;29], which is a geometric representation of the *calculus of variations*. Even though we will not make *explicit* use of it here, the marginal value theorem is sufficiently general that it can be applied to modelling of reaction times under choice uncertainty[55] and to neural information theory.

4.3. Paying with Spikes

As we have seen, a neuron represents two distinct types of cost: *variable* and *fixed* (baseline). The fixed cost is the energy required to build a neuron plus the power required to maintain it whereas the variable cost is the power required to generate spikes at different firing rates. Much of our exploration of the cost of information involves vision, so we begin with a brief overview of the visual system (see Figure 4.2).

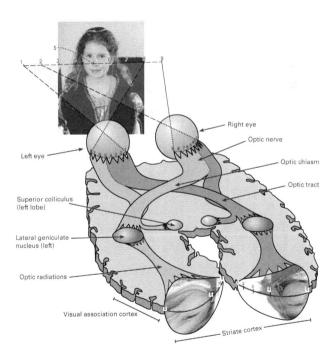

Figure 4.2. Horizontal section through the visual system. The optic nerve consists of retinal ganglion cell axons, which synapse at the lateral geniculate nucleus (LGN); this projects to the striate cortex. From Stone (2012)[116].

45

The eye sends about 10 million bits/s to the brain via the 1 million retinal ganglion cell axons which comprise the optic nerve[60]. Retinal ganglion cells and their postsynaptic targets in the *lateral geniculate nucleus* (LGN) provide between 1.5 and 4.5 bits/spike about the retinal image[50], which is consistent with the theoretical prediction of 3 bits/spike mentioned in Section 3.7.

According to Equation 3.5, the coding capacity R_{max} of a neuron with a mean firing rate of $\bar{y}$ spikes/s is $R_{max} \approx \bar{y} \log 1/(\bar{y}\,\Delta t)$ bits/s, where this function is plotted in Figure 4.3a. This shows how the coding capacity of a neuron increases with mean firing rate, which is proportional to its diameter. For example, if the firing rate is $\bar{y} = 15$ spikes/s then the coding capacity is 91 bits/s. If the firing rate is doubled to $\bar{y} = 30$ spikes/s then the coding capacity is not doubled to 182 bits/s but increases to $\approx 30 \log 1/(30 \times 0.001) = 152$ bits/s. And if we wanted to double the coding capacity then, according to Figure 4.3a, we would have to increase the firing rate to about 40 spikes/s. Thus, in this example, doubling capacity requires tripling the firing rate.

4.4. Paying with Hardware

The data analysed in this chapter are derived mainly from Perge et al. (2009)[88]. These authors provide a detailed examination of the optic nerve of the adult male guinea pig, which is the bundle of 100,000 ganglion cell axons connecting each retina to the brain (see Figure 4.2

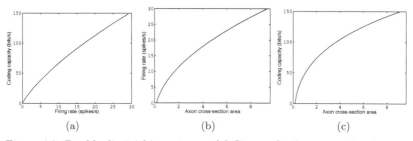

(a)   (b)   (c)

Figure 4.3. Doubly diminishing returns. (a) Given a fixed cross-sectional area A, the coding capacity increases sublinearly with firing rate (Equation 3.5). (b) The mean firing rate increases with $\sqrt{\text{cross-sectional area}}$ (Equation 4.4). (c) Combined effects of (a) and (b) dictate that coding capacity increases very slowly with cross-sectional area (Equation 4.5, $\Delta t = 1$ms).

for the human equivalent). These axons are unmyelinated within the retina, but they acquire a myelin sheath as they join the optic nerve. This allows properties of unmyelinated and myelinated axons to be compared within the same population of neurons.

Perge et al. (2009)[88] found that the mean firing rate $\bar{y}$ increases in proportion to axon diameter d:

$$\bar{y} \quad = \quad k(d - d_{min}) \text{ spikes/s}, \tag{4.2}$$

where k is a constant and d_{min} is the diameter of the thinnest axon. The parameter values are $k = 10$ and $d_{min} = 0.46\,\mu m$ for myelinated axons (excluding myelin sheath), and $k = 13$ and $d_{min} = 0.32\,\mu m$ for unmyelinated neurons. For simplicity, we use values for myelinated axons below. Substituting Equation 4.2 into 3.5, coding capacity is

$$R_{max} \quad \approx \quad -k(d - d_{min}) \log k(d - d_{min}) \, \Delta t \text{ bits/s}. \tag{4.3}$$

We can estimate how axonal cross-sectional area A and mean firing rate are related by substituting $d = 2(A/\pi)^{1/2}$ into Equation 4.2:

$$\bar{y} \quad = \quad k(2(A/\pi)^{1/2} - d_{min}) \text{ spikes/s}, \tag{4.4}$$

as shown in Figure 4.3b. Substituting Equation 4.4 into Equation 3.5 yields an equation which specifies how the coding capacity of a neuron

(a)   (b)

Figure 4.4. A coding capacity of $R_{max} = 150$ bits/s can be obtained using either: (a) an axon with a cross-sectional area of $A = 8.5\mu m^2$; or (b) three thin axons with a collective area of $3\,\mu m^2$ (drawn to scale).

increases with its cross-sectional area:

$$R_{max} \approx -k \left(2(A/\pi)^{1/2} - d_{min}\right) \log \left(2(A/\pi)^{1/2} - d_{min}\right) k \, \Delta t, \quad (4.5)$$

shown in Figure 4.3c. For example, if doubling a neuron's coding capacity requires that its mean firing rate increases by a factor of three then its area A must increase by a factor of nine.

We can make use of Figure 4.3c (and Equations 4.4 and 4.5) to show that it is more economical to have several thin axons rather than one thick axon (all figures are approximate here). For example, a single neuron with an axonal cross-sectional area of $A \approx 8.5 \, \mu m^2$ would have a mean firing rate of 29 spikes/s and a coding capacity of $R_{max} = 150$ bits/s. However, a neuron with an axon area of only $A \approx 1 \, \mu m^2$ would have a mean firing rate of 7 spikes/s and a coding capacity of $R_{max} = 50$ bits/s. Therefore, three neurons with a collective axon area of $A \approx 3 \, \mu m^2$ and a collective firing rate of $3 \times 7 = 21$ spikes/s have the same coding capacity as a single axon with $A \approx 8.5 \, \mu m^2$ firing at 29 spikes/s (Figure 4.4). However, thin axons have higher noise levels[42], which reduce mutual information (Equation 2.15). So the different axon diameters observed in different brain regions (Section 4.7) probably represent a compromise between mutual information rate and collective axon diameter.

In summary, there are two types of diminishing returns here: first, the diminishing information returns on the variable cost of increasing firing rate (Equation 3.5, Figure 4.3a); second, the diminishing mean firing rate returns on the fixed cost of increasing cross-sectional area (Equation 4.4, Figure 4.3b). Consequently, coding capacity increases very slowly with cross-sectional area (Equation 4.5, Figure 4.3c).

4.5. Paying with Power

In the next few pages, we explore how coding capacity, power, and firing rate are related. In order to do this, we need to estimate the energy cost of a single spike. Within the brain, energy is measured in units of *adenosine triphosphate* (ATP) molecules. These are supplied by *mitochondria*, which are elongated *organelles* (3.2 by $0.22 \, \mu m$) within each neuron, where the width of a mitochondrion effectively sets a lower limit on the diameter of a neuron's axon. When a spike passes along an axon, sodium ions enter, and potassium ions exit through the neuron's membrane. The main cost of a spike involves pumping those ions back across the membrane using energy derived from ATP. For unmyelinated axons, the energy cost of a spike increases in proportion to axon diameter, but for myelinated axons, the cost per spike does not vary with diameter[88].

Within each ganglion cell axon of the optic nerve, each spike requires 400 ATP molecules for each micrometre (μm) of myelinated axon[88], and each molecule of ATP provides about 10^{-19} Joules[80]. The speed of spikes in unmyelinated ganglion cell axons is about 2 m/s, whereas it is about 6 m/s for a typical diameter of 0.7 μm[88].

Assuming a speed of 6 m/s, the power required to sustain a single spike in a myelinated ganglion cell axon is

$$\gamma \quad = \quad (6 \times 10^6 \ \mu\text{m/s}) \times (400 \times 10^{-19} \ \text{J/}\mu\text{m}) \qquad (4.6)$$
$$= \quad 240 \ \text{pJ/s}, \qquad (4.7)$$

where pJ stands for pico-Joule, and $1\text{pJ} = 10^{-12}$ J.

Now we can return to the problem of estimating the energy cost of information. If the energy required to transmit one spike along an axon is $\gamma = 240$ pJ/s then the power required for a firing rate of y spikes/s is

$$E_{spike} \quad = \quad \gamma y \ \text{pJ/s}. \qquad (4.8)$$

Clearly, the rate at which spikes can be transmitted by a neuron is limited by the amount of available power, which is limited by the number of mitochondria per millimetre of axon, and this (in turn) is limited by axon cross-sectional area. If the power available for generating spikes is E_{spike} pJ/s then (from Equation 4.8) the maximum firing rate is $y_{max} = E_{spike}/\gamma$ spikes/s. Substituting this into Equation 3.5 yields coding capacity as a function of the cost E_{spike} of y_{max} spikes/s for myelinated neurons (as shown in Figure 4.5a),

$$R_{max} \quad \approx \quad \frac{E_{spike}}{\gamma} \log \frac{1}{\Delta t \ (E_{spike}/\gamma)} \ \text{bits/s}. \qquad (4.9)$$

The results provided above are consistent with results for visually responsive *large monopolar cells* (LMCs) in flies (see Chapter 8). LMCs are non-spiking neurons with high metabolic rates and correspondingly high information rates, as shown in Figure 4.5b. This shows the total (i.e. fixed plus variable) cost of mutual information rates, across four different species of fly, reported in Niven et al. (2007)[83]. There is an obvious qualitative similarity between Figures 4.5a and 4.5b, despite the fact that Figure 4.5a shows coding capacity whereas Figure 4.5b shows mutual information.

The diminishing information returns on firing rate and axon diameter suggest a trade-off between information and energy. In the remainder of this chapter, we explore how this trade-off predicts particular values for axon diameter, the distribution of axon diameters, mean firing rate, the distribution of firing rates, and synaptic conductance.

4.6. Optimal Axon Diameter

As stated above, energy is not only used to pay for spikes, it also pays for the substantial neuronal hardware required to transmit those spikes. If an organism seeks to minimise the overall cost of information then its neurons should have evolved to minimise this cost. Perge et al.

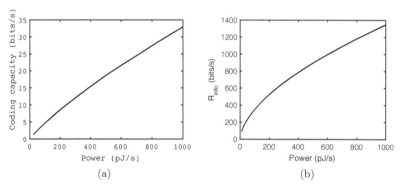

Figure 4.5. (a) How coding capacity increases as a function of power in myelinated ganglion cell axons (Equation 4.9), based on Perge et al. (2009)[88]. (b) How mutual information scales with total power for large monopolar cells (LMCs). Derived from Figure 7 in Niven et al. (2007)[83].

(2009)[88] showed that the equations defined in the preceding section can be used to evaluate metabolic efficiency, as follows.

To address this problem, we need two equations. First, we need an equation which expresses how mutual information increases with axon diameter d. Second, we need an equation which describes how power (E) increases with d. Then, we can divide the first equation by the second to obtain a function $\varepsilon(d)$ which expresses how efficiency (measured in bits/pJ) varies with axonal diameter d.

For the equation which describes how mutual information I increases with diameter, we substitute Equation 4.2 into Equation 3.5, and recalling (from Section 3.6) that $I = \epsilon R_{max}$,

$$I \approx \epsilon k(d - d_{min}) \log \frac{1}{k(d - d_{min}) \, \Delta t} \quad \text{bits/s}, \qquad (4.10)$$

where $k = 10$ (Equation 4.2) for myelinated neurons. For the equation which describes how power (E) increases with diameter, we make use of the fact that the total power output of a neuron increases linearly with the number of mitochondria per cubic millimetre, which increases in proportion to d^2. More precisely, Perge et al. (2009)[88] found that the total volume per millimetre occupied by mitochondria or *mitochondrial volume* in retinal ganglion cells is

$$V_m = \alpha(d - d_{min}) \times [(d - d_{min}) + \beta] \; \mu\text{m}^3/\text{mm}. \qquad (4.11)$$

This effectively measures *power capacity* in units of mitochondrial volume per millimetre of axon. The main thing to notice is that V_m increases with the square of diameter, that is, in proportion to axon area. The values of the constants α and β were estimated for myelinated and unmyelinated sections of the same retinal ganglion cells. For myelinated axons, the constants were $\alpha = 0.0044 \mu\text{m}$ and $\beta = 4.7 \mu\text{m}$; for unmyelinated axons, they were $\alpha = 0.017 \mu\text{m}$ and $\beta = 2.5 \mu\text{m}$. The smallest diameter was estimated as $d_{min} = 0.46 \mu\text{m}$ for myelinated and $d_{min} = 0.44 \mu\text{m}$ for unmyelinated neurons (these estimates were obtained differently from those of Equation 4.2). The estimated values of α and β imply that power output increases more rapidly in unmyelinated than in myelinated axons, as shown in Figure 4.6a.

The mitochondrial volume is proportional to the cost of spike generation, but this takes no account of the fixed cost κ of maintaining a neuron. Accordingly, the total cost is

$$E \;=\; \kappa + V_m \quad \mu m^3/mm, \tag{4.12}$$

where κ is expressed in energy-equivalent units of mitochondrial volume. Substituting Equation 4.11 in 4.12 yields

$$E \;=\; \alpha(d - d_{min}) \times [(d - d_{min}) + \beta] + \kappa \quad \mu m^3/mm. \tag{4.13}$$

Because Equation 4.13 is proportional to energy, it could be expressed in pico-Joules (pJ) using a constant. However, we are primarily interested in knowing which diameter maximises efficiency, so we can set this constant to unity. This expresses E in arbitrary units, which we will call pJ/s, as a reminder that E represents power. The metabolic efficiency $\varepsilon(d)$ (number of bits obtained per pJ of energy) at a given axon diameter d (with a mean firing rate given by Equation 4.2) is

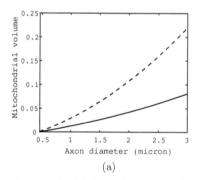
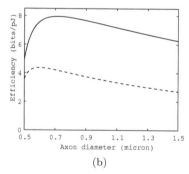

(a)   (b)

Figure 4.6. (a) Mitochondrial volume versus axon diameter for myelinated (solid line) and unmyelinated (dashed line) segments of the retinal ganglion cells (Equation 4.11). Data derived from Perge et al. (2009)[88].
(b) Metabolic efficiency ε (mutual information per Joule) versus axon diameter d for myelinated (solid line) and unmyelinated (dashed line) axons. If $\kappa=0.0015$ and $\Delta t=5$ ms as in Perge et al. (2009) then (using Equation 4.14) ε peaks at $d=0.72\,\mu m$ for myelinated axons and $0.60\,\mu m$ for unmyelinated axons. Power is in relative units. Based on Figure 9b in Perge et al. (2009)[88].

$\varepsilon(d) = I/E$ bits/pJ. Substituting Equations 4.10 and 4.13 yields

$$\varepsilon(d) \quad = \quad \frac{\epsilon k(d - d_{min}) \log \frac{1}{k(d-d_{min})\,\Delta t}}{\alpha(d - d_{min}) \times [(d - d_{min}) + \beta] + \kappa} \quad \text{bits/pJ.} \quad (4.14)$$

Assuming parameter values for myelinated neurons, the maximum value of ε corresponds to $d = 0.7\,\mu$m (Figure 4.6b), the most common axon diameter found in the visual neurons under study. The assumed value for κ is $0.0015\,\mu$m^3 (as in Perge et al., 2009[88]), which is similar to values observed in the thinnest axons (i.e. $d \approx 0.5\,\mu$m). In summary, this account of results presented in Perge et al. (2009) suggests that, for neurons in the optic nerve, the most common axon diameter maximises the number of bits transmitted per Joule of energy expended. A more detailed discussion can be found in Perge et al. (2012)[89].

4.7. Optimal Distribution of Axon Diameters

Given the constraints described above, we should expect axons to have a particular diameter. Additionally, we should expect that axons should all have the *same* diameter. However, when axons are measured within bundles of axons like the optic nerve, they are found to contain axons with a characteristic distribution of axon diameters, shown in Figure 4.7. This shows that most axons are thin ($<1\,\mu$m), but they are mixed with a small proportion of thicker axons.

The distribution of axon diameters observed in neuron bundles is typically modelled as a *log normal distribution* (Equation 8.5), which has the same shape as depicted in Figure 4.7. The general shape of this

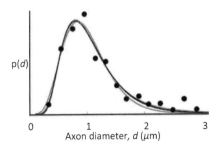

Figure 4.7. Distribution of axon diameters (dots), fitted with Equation 4.15. Reproduced with permission from Pajevic and Basser (2013)[86].

distribution matches nerve bundles found in disparate brain regions[89], such as the optic nerve, which carries information from the eye; the fornix, which connects the hippocampus to the hypothalamus; parallel fibres of granule cells in the cerebellum; olfactory axons; and the corpus callosum, which connects the two hemispheres of the brain[86]; but not auditory axons[89]. However, a recent information-theoretic analysis by Pajevic and Basser (2013)[86] suggests that other distributions may provide more accurate models of the distribution of axon diameters.

Let us suppose that each neuron bundle consists of a particular distribution $p(d)$ of neuron axon diameters, where $p(d)$ specifies the exact proportion of neurons at each diameter d. Given certain physical constraints, the form of $p(d)$ can be obtained using the calculus of variations. The calculus of variations allows us to specify constraints as hard limits on parameters (e.g. bundle cross-sectional area, total number of axons) and then to find the best possible value for a quantity of interest (e.g. coding capacity).

If the number N of axons is used as a hard limit then the distribution of axon diameters which maximises the total amount of information transmitted is given by Pajevic and Basser's Equation 5 (with $k=1$),

$$p(d) \quad = \quad (c/d)e^{-(a/d)+bd}. \tag{4.15}$$

When this function was fitted to empirical data[86], typical values for the parameters were found to be $a \approx 3$ and $b \approx 5$, which give the same general form as a log-normal distribution (c is a normalisation constant). Note that this does not predict that axons should have the same diameters in different bundles but that the *distribution* of diameters should conform to Equation 4.15. Pajevic and Basser's statistical analysis indicates that their equation provides a significantly better fit than a log-normal curve to the distributions of axon diameters from a wide variety of brain regions[86], with one example shown in Figure 4.7.

The constraint on neuron number N can be interpreted as a constraint on the overall (i.e. fixed plus average variable) cost of a neuron bundle. And because Equation 4.15 maximises information throughput subject to this constraint, it therefore maximises the average information throughput per neuron. This seems to ignore the variable cost of particular firing rates, but we know that the mean firing rate is proportional to axon diameter (Equation 4.2). We can therefore interpret Equation 4.15 as the distribution of axon diameters and mean firing rates which maximises information per Joule, where this energy is expended as fixed cost (i.e. building plus resting metabolic cost) and variable costs (i.e. mean firing rate cost). Thus, with some reservations, we can conclude that the distribution of axon diameters observed in physiological nerve bundles maximises metabolic efficiency.

4.8. Axon Diameter and Spike Speed

If we consider a neuron to be a communication channel then the rate at which information is transmitted along its axon depends on two factors: (1) the firing rate y and (2) the spike speed or *conduction velocity v* at which spikes travel through an axon. Clearly, both firing rate and conduction velocity matter, but they are different types of quantities, and they matter in different ways. Increasing the firing rate increases coding capacity and therefore reduces the time required to integrate information about a neuron's input (e.g. on the retina) once it arrives at the output. In contrast, increasing conduction velocity reduces the amount of time it takes for spikes (and therefore information) to travel from the neuron's input to its output.

Just as we can quantify how coding capacity is related to firing rate, so we can quantify how the conduction velocity of spikes is related to axonal cross-sectional area. Neurons with diameters below about 0.5μm are usually unmyelinated, with relatively slow conduction velocities (about 1 m/s in the optic nerve[88]). Velocity increases in proportion to the square root of diameter in unmyelinated neurons[33], $v \propto d^{1/2}$. For example, doubling the conduction velocity of an unmyelinated neuron requires the cross-sectional area to be increased by a factor of $2^4 = 16$.

In contrast, neurons with diameters above about $0.5\,\mu$m are usually myelinated, with conduction velocities between 1 and 36 m/s in the optic nerve[88]. In these neurons, conduction velocity increases in proportion to diameter[33], such that increasing axon diameter by $1\,\mu$m increases conduction velocity by about 9 m/s. Thus, doubling conduction velocity in myelinated neurons requires cross-sectional area to be increased by a factor of $2^2 = 4$.

In both myelinated and unmyelinated axons, the mean firing rate increases with diameter, $\bar{y} \propto d$. In myelinated axons, the power required for each spike does not increase with diameter (or at a very low rate[88]). Given that $\bar{y} \propto d$ and $v \propto d$, the total power required to sustain both of these relationships increases with d^2. This is consistent with the power capacity V_m provided by mitochondrial volume (where $V_m \propto d^2$).

In contrast, the power required for each spike increases with diameter d in unmyelinated axons[88]. Given that $\bar{y} \propto d$ and $v \propto d^{1/2}$, the total power required increases with $d^{2.5}$, but power capacity $V_m \propto d^2$; so unmyelinated neurons may be starved of power. This may explain why the physiological values of the constants in Equation 4.11 ensure that power capacity increases more rapidly (with diameter) in unmyelinated axons than in myelinated axons (Figure 4.6a).

The practical consequences of different spike speeds may be negligible because axons within the brain are typically very short, as discussed in Perge et al. (2012)[89]. For example, the distance from the eye to the first synapse within the brain (the lateral geniculate nucleus) is so short (17 mm in a guinea pig) that the difference in conduction times between the thinnest and thickest axons is only[60] 3.2 ms. This is similar to the smallest interval between spikes, and is considerably shorter than the typical temporal response variability (10–30 ms) observed with repetitions of a stimulus[79] (see Section 3.8).

Thus, over short distances, increased spike speeds reduce arrival times by an amount which is well within the range of arrival times caused by normal temporal 'jitter' (i.e. noise). It therefore seems unlikely that conduction velocity is a major factor in determining axon diameters within the brain. However, control of fine movements requires rapid feedback from (long) peripheral sensory neurons[72]. This is probably why spikes from muscle receptors travel at 100 m/s, which requires thick, myelinated axons, 8–17 μm in diameter.

In summary, a given coding capacity can be obtained expensively from a single thick axon or cheaply by sharing this capacity between many thin axons (but with a lower signal-to-noise ratio per axon[42]).

In contrast, fast spike speeds require thick axons, and these fast speeds cannot be obtained by sharing spikes between thin axons, which transmit spikes slowly. Thus, large coding capacities can be obtained cheaply using several thin axons, but no such trickery is available for spike speed; high spike speeds can only be obtained with thick axons[89].

4.9. Optimal Mean Firing Rate

The maximum coding capacity of a neuron occurs when its mean firing rate is half the maximum firing rate (see Section 3.4). But neurons usually have mean firing rates which are much lower than their maximum firing rates. Here, we analyse the amount of energy required at different mean firing rates to show that the low mean firing rates observed physiologically provide information at the lowest energy cost possible. The following account is based on Levy and Baxter (1996)[70] (see also Rieke et al., 1997[98]).

If we measure spikes during an interval of Δt seconds then the observed firing rates have discrete values $y = \{0, 1/\Delta t, \ldots, n_{max}/\Delta t\}$, where n_{max} is the maximum number of spikes that can be generated by a particular neuron in Δt seconds. In Section 4.10, we will discover that the distribution of firing rates with maximum coding capacity is the discrete exponential distribution (Figure 4.8). In this case, the coding capacity of a neuron with a mean firing rate $\overline{y}$ is defined by the

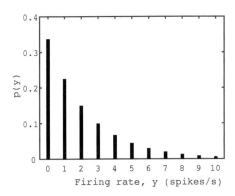

Figure 4.8. The discrete exponential distribution of firing rates has maximum entropy (Equation 4.21, with $\overline{y} = 2$ spikes/s and $\Delta t = 1$ s).

maximum entropy reward function[70;98]

$$R_{max} \quad = \quad (1/\Delta t + \overline{y})\log(1 + \overline{y}\Delta t) \; - \; \overline{y}\log(\overline{y}\Delta t) \; \text{ bits/s, (4.16)}$$

where $\overline{y}\Delta t$ is the average number of spikes observed in Δt seconds.

As discussed above, the total power E required for a neuron firing at a mean rate of $\overline{y}$ spikes/s comprises two components, E_{rest} and E_{spike}. The component E_{spike} is the power required to generate spikes. In contrast, E_{rest} is the total power required to maintain a neuron in its resting state, and includes the power required by *glial cells*, which form the myelin sheath. Thus, the cost function is

$$E \quad = \quad E_{rest} + E_{spike} \; \text{ pJ/s.} \qquad (4.17)$$

If increasing the firing rate by 1 spike/s requires an additional γ pJ/s then (using Equation 4.8) the power required to generate $\overline{y}$ spikes/s is $E_{spike} = \gamma \overline{y}$ pJ/s. Substituting Equations 4.16 and 4.17 into Equation 4.1 defines the *maximum entropy efficiency function,*

$$\varepsilon_H \quad = \quad \frac{(1/\Delta t + \overline{y})\log(1 + \overline{y}\Delta t) \; - \; \overline{y}\log(\overline{y}\Delta t)}{E_{rest} + \gamma\overline{y}} \; \text{ bits/pJ. (4.18)}$$

In order to evaluate E_{rest} and E_{spike}, we depart from Levy and Baxter's analysis and use parameter values of E_{rest} and γ reported in Attwell and Laughlin (2001)[9], based on the cost of spikes in rat neocortical pyramidal neurons.

In the absence of any spiking activity, each neuron requires $E_{rest} = 4.44 \times 10^8$ ATP/s. Given that each ATP molecule supplies about 10^{-19} J of energy, $E_{rest} \approx 44.4$ pJ/s. Every time the firing rate increases by 1 spike/s, the power required[9] increases by $1.6 \times E_{rest}$, so that $\gamma \approx 71$ pJ/s. Therefore, Equation 4.17 evaluates to

$$E \quad \approx \quad 44.4 + 71\overline{y} \; \text{ pJ/s.} \qquad (4.19)$$

Equation 4.8 implies that the mean firing rate is $\overline{y} = E_{spike}/\gamma$ spikes/s, which, when substituted in Equation 4.16, yields the maximum entropy reward function in terms of E_{spike},

$$R_{max} = [(1/\Delta t + (E_{spike}/\gamma))\log(1 + (E_{spike}/\gamma)\Delta t)$$
$$- (E_{spike}/\gamma)\log((E_{spike}/\gamma)\Delta t)] \quad \text{bits/s, (4.20)}$$

as shown in Figure 4.9a. Substituting Equations 4.19 and 4.20 in Equation 4.1 expresses the maximum entropy metabolic efficiency in terms of spiking power E_{spike}, as shown in Figure 4.9d.

The maximum entropy efficiency function, expressed in terms of the firing rate (Equation 4.18), can be evaluated by substituting Equation 4.19 in 4.18. From Figure 4.10a, the maximum metabolic efficiency of $\varepsilon_H \approx 0.06$ bits/pJ is obtained at a firing rate of $\overline{y}_M^* \approx 2$ spikes/s. Using Equation 4.19, a firing rate of 2 spikes/s requires 186 pJ/s. Thus, at a

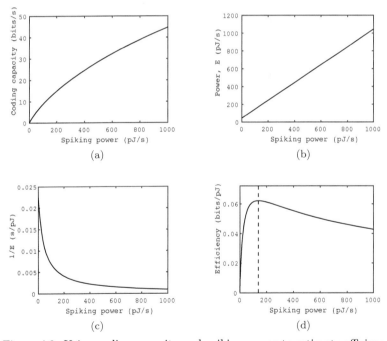

Figure 4.9. Using coding capacity and spiking power to estimate efficiency. (a) Coding capacity R_{max} increases with diminishing returns on spiking power E_{spike} pJ/s (Equation 4.20). (b) Power required for $\overline{y}$ spikes/s is $E = E_{rest} + E_{spike}$ pJ/s (Equation 4.19). (c) Time $1/E$ required to deliver 1 pJ decreases rapidly as E increases. (d) Efficiency $\varepsilon_H = R_{max} \times 1/E$.

mean firing rate of $\overline{y}_M^* = 2$ spikes/s, each spike provides 5.6 bits/spike ($186/2$ pJ/spike $\times$ 0.06 bits/pJ), similar to values estimated for other neurons [50]. A theoretical analysis by Johnson et al. (2016) [56] suggests that a metabolically efficient neural code is consistent with the average firing rates observed in cortical neurons. On a related note, Gaudry and Reinagel (2007) [46] conclude that neural coding (of contrast) conserves information per spike rather than information per second, consistent with metabolic efficiency.

In Figure 4.10b, key parameters at the maximum metabolic efficiency firing rate $\overline{y}_M^* = 2$ spikes/s are compared to their values at the maximum coding efficiency firing rate of $\overline{y}_C^* = (\text{max firing rate})/2 = 0.5/\Delta t = 20$ spikes/s, using Equations 4.16–4.18. At $\overline{y}_M^*$ spikes/s, the spike, information, and energy rates are about one tenth of their values at $\overline{y}_C^*$, but metabolic efficiency is almost twice as high at $\overline{y}_M^*$ relative to metabolic efficiency at $\overline{y}_C^*$. Simulations by the author yielded results very similar to those in Figure 4.10 if R_{max} is estimated using Equation 3.8 instead of Equation 4.16; this suggests that the constraint of a maximum entropy distribution of firing rates (Equation 4.16) has little effect on the firing rate that maximises metabolic efficiency.

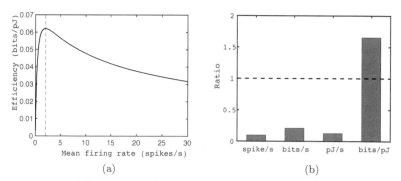

(a)   (b)

Figure 4.10. Efficiency and firing rate in rat neocortical pyramidal neurons.
(a) Maximum entropy efficiency function vs mean firing rate (Equation 4.18, with Δt=2.5ms).
(b) Ratio of [performance at maximum metabolic efficiency firing rate ($\overline{y}_M^*$=2 spikes/s)] divided by [performance at maximum information firing rate ($\overline{y}_C^*$ spikes/s)]. Bars from left to right show the ratio of firing rate ($\overline{y}_M^*/\overline{y}_C^*$), information rate, power, and metabolic efficiency.

4.10. Optimal Distribution of Firing Rates

If the mean firing rate is fixed at a particular value (and given that the firing rate cannot be negative) then what is the optimal *distribution* of firing rates for a single neuron? The answer is implicit in Section 2.4, where it is stated that the maximum entropy distribution is exponential (Figure 2.5b). Specifically, if the mean firing rate is $\bar{y}$ spikes/s and if spikes are counted for a period of Δt seconds then the maximum entropy firing distribution of spike counts n is[70;98] (Figure 4.8)

$$p_E(n) = (1 - e^{-\lambda}) e^{-\lambda n}, \qquad (4.21)$$

where $\lambda = \ln[1 + (\bar{y}\Delta t)^{-1}]$. For a given mean firing rate, λ is constant, so Equation 4.21 is an exponential distribution (i.e. $p_E(n) \propto e^{-n}$, where $n=y\Delta t$). This is supported by Baddeley et al. (1997)[10], who found that neocortical pyramidal cells have exponential firing rate distributions. The constraint of a fixed mean firing rate amounts to a constraint on power, so (ignoring baseline costs) the distribution that maximises entropy also maximises metabolic efficiency.

Note that the optimal (log-normal) firing rate distribution derived in Section 4.7 refers to a distribution across different neurons, whereas the optimal (exponential) firing rate distribution derived here refers to a single neuron.

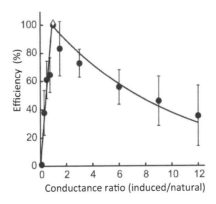

Figure 4.11. Maximum metabolic efficiency is obtained at the natural conductance value observed in neuronal synapses. Reproduced with permission from Harris et al. (2015)[50].

4.11. Optimal Synaptic Conductance

Compelling support for metabolic efficiency is provided in Harris et al. (2015)[50]. In this study, the conductances of synapses between the optic nerve and the brain (specifically, the *lateral geniculate nucleus*, see Figure 4.2) were artificially changed from their natural values, and the (mutual) information transmitted per Joule was measured at each conductance level. It was found that each synapse transmits most information per Joule at its natural conductance (Figure 4.11): 15.6 bits per 10^8 ATP molecules. This elegant experiment suggests that synaptic conductances are optimised to transmit as much information per Joule as possible.

4.12. Summary

For single neurons, we have considered how coding capacity increases slowly with energy expended on spikes and neural hardware, and why a fundamental law of information theory (Equation 2.22) means that it is not possible to do better than the logarithmic increase in coding capacity with energy expended. The vagaries of neuronal architecture dictate that the cost of coding capacity increases even more steeply than specified by this law. Probably because of this, the most metabolically efficient axon diameter matches the most common axon diameter observed physiologically. We found that neuron bundles from diverse brain regions contain a similar skewed distribution of axon diameters, which allows neuron bundles to provide information at the lowest overall energy cost.

We then explored why axons have different diameters, and our analysis suggested that (within the brain) larger axon diameters exist not to transmit spikes at high speed but to transmit information with a high signal-to-noise ratio. Assuming a maximum entropy (i.e. exponential) distribution of firing rates, we found that the mean firing rate that maximises metabolic efficiency matches physiological firing rates and is much lower than the firing rate that maximises information rate. Finally, the cost of transmitting information across synapses in the visual system was found to be metabolically efficient.

Chapter 5

Encoding Colour

We claim that the results of a quantitative approach are sufficiently extreme that they begin to alter our qualitative conception of how the nervous system works.
Rieke, Warland, de Ruyter van Steveninck, and Bialek, 1997.

5.1. Introduction

Colour aftereffects have a long history in the study of perception. However, as far back as the 18th century, it was known that colours and their aftereffects come in unique pairs[45]. Specifically, staring at a green colour induces a red aftereffect (and vice versa), whereas staring at a blue colour induces a yellow aftereffect (and vice versa). In order to experience these aftereffects, see https://goo.gl/r8Ka4d.

How these red–green and blue–yellow aftereffects occur can be explained reasonably easily in terms of physiological mechanisms, as we shall see. But it is less easy to explain *why* there is a red–green and a blue–yellow aftereffect, but no red–blue aftereffect (for example).

In this chapter, we will discover that information theory and neural efficiency does not predict how these aftereffects should be implemented as biological mechanisms. But information theory does predict that whichever mechanism is used to encode colour, it should represent colour as red–green and blue–yellow pairs[5]. Before we can consider this in more detail, we need to know about the anatomy of the eye.

5.2. The Eye

In the human eye, the retina lies about 20 mm behind the lens (Figure 1.2). The retinal image is registered by two types of photoreceptors, *cones* and *rods*. Cones operate under daylight conditions and mediate colour vision, whereas rods operate under night-time conditions but provide no colour vision. The cones dominate a small circular region called the *fovea*, where we see most detail. The fovea is 0.5 mm in diameter and contains 200,000 cones per square millimetre.

The amount of light absorbed at each wavelength by each cone type defines its *tuning curve*, as shown in Figure 5.1. Cones sensitive to long wavelength light (which looks red) are conventionally labelled L-cones, cones sensitive to medium wavelengths (which look green) are labelled M-cones, and cones sensitive to short wavelengths (which look blue) are labelled S-cones. However, for simplicity, we will refer to these as red, green, and blue cones. In reality, blue cones are insensitive and have a maximum about 10% of the height shown in Figure 5.1.

All biological lenses suffer from *chromatic aberration*, because lenses split light into its constituent wavelengths, like a prism. Consequently, only a small band of wavelengths (colours) can be brought to a focus, and all other wavelengths form a superposition of blurred images on the retina. In humans, the band of wavelengths brought to a focus matches

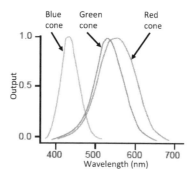

Figure 5.1. Tuning curves of cones sensitive to short (blue), medium (green), and long (red) light wavelengths, with peak sensitivities at 560 nm, 530 nm, and 430 nm, respectively. There are three types of cones, sensitive to long, medium, and short wavelengths of light, but only cones sensitive to long and medium wavelengths inhabit the fovea. The overall proportions of cones sensitive to red, green, and blue light are 63%, 31%, and 6%, respectively.

the peak of the red and green cone tuning curves, so that wavelengths which match the blue cone tuning curve form a blue, blurred image on the retina. The poor quality of the information conveyed by this blue image may well account for the rarity of blue cones in the retina and for their virtual absence in the fovea (see also Balasubramanian, 2015[12]). This absence means that we are at liberty to consider only red and green cones for the present. Notice that the similarity of the red and green tuning curves minimises the effects of chromatic aberration whilst allowing different wavelengths to be discriminated.

Retinal Ganglion Cells and Receptive Fields. In order for any neuron to respond to light which falls on a particular part of the retinal image, it seems self-evident that the neuron must be connected, either directly or via other neurons, to photoreceptors in that part of the retina. One important class of neurons is the *retinal ganglion cell*. There are 1 million ganglion cells in each retina, and their axons form the optic nerve, which transmits information from 126 million photoreceptors in each eye to the brain (see Figure 4.2). Each ganglion cell is connected, via intermediate layers of *bipolar* and *horizontal* neurons within the retina, to its own roughly circular region of the retina. This region is called a *receptive field* (see Figure 5.2), a term coined by Hartline (1967)[51]. A neuron's output is affected by light that falls within its receptive field, whereas light outside of its receptive field has little or no effect.

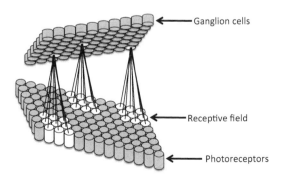

Ganglion cells

Receptive field

Photoreceptors

Figure 5.2. Each ganglion cell receives inputs from a set of photoreceptors which define its receptive field, via layers of neurons (not shown). In vertebrates, light passes through these layers to reach the photoreceptors.

5.3. How Aftereffects Occur

It was stated earlier that explaining how colour aftereffects arise is easy. Accordingly, the following is the standard textbook explanation for how a colour aftereffect mechanism could be designed in principle. Specifically, Figure 5.3 shows how the outputs of red, green, and blue cones can be recombined to explain how aftereffects occur. Red and green cone outputs can be added to form the output of a ganglion cell; because superimposed red and green light looks yellow, this ganglion cell acts like a yellow, or *red+green sum channel*. Similarly, the outputs of red and green cones can be subtracted by a ganglion cell whose output increases in response to red light and decreases in response to green light and so acts like a *red–green difference channel*. Finally, if a ganglion cell has an input which is the difference between blue cone outputs and yellow channel outputs then this ganglion cell acts like a *blue–yellow difference channel*. In practice, the response characteristics of ganglion cells are difficult to measure, but we can be reasonably certain that different classes of ganglion cells can implement the sum and difference channels described above (see Section 5.12).

It has long been recognised that perception of colour depends on the *relative* amounts of red and green light entering the eye. This translates fairly directly into the relative outputs of the red and green

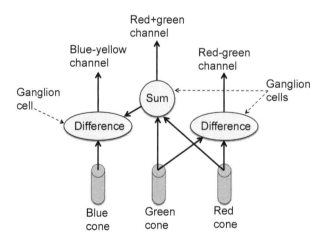

Figure 5.3. Schematic diagram of how outputs from three cone types are combined to produce three new colour channels (ganglion cell outputs).

cones, and the mechanism thought to underpin colour perception is known as *opponent processing*. Accordingly, if the outputs of red cones are greater than those of green cones then we see red, and vice versa.

Now consider how opponent processing can give rise to a red–green colour aftereffect. Exposure to a white disc (which contains red and green light) activates both red and green channels equally and therefore results in the perception of white, as shown in Figure 5.4a. Exposure to a red disc yields a large output from the red channel but a baseline output from the green channel (Figure 5.4b). After a few seconds, the red channel adapts, which effectively makes the red channel less sensitive to subsequent inputs. Thus, after adaptation, exposure to a white disc yields red channel outputs which are less than green channel outputs, resulting in a green aftereffect. A similar line of reasoning explains how the red aftereffect and the blue–yellow aftereffects occur.

This explains how colour aftereffects can arise, but it does not explain why (1) colours are encoded as sums and differences (i.e. opponent pairs) or (2) there is a red–green and a blue–yellow pairing rather than (for example) a red–blue and a green–yellow pairing. The short answer to both questions is that sum–difference encoding allows efficient use of the available channel capacity. Question (1) is explored next, and question (2) is addressed in Section 5.12.

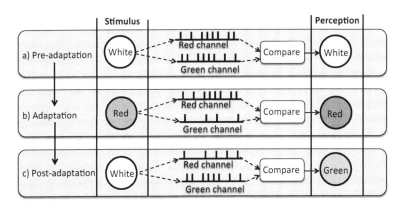

Figure 5.4. A model of *how* colour aftereffects occur. (a) A white disc activates both red and green cones equally, so white is seen. (b) Adaptation to red activates red cones, so red is seen. (c) Adaptation reduces sensitivity of red cones so that exposure to white activates green cones more than red cones, and a green aftereffect is seen.

5.4. The Problem with Colour

Neighbouring red and green cones in the retina have similar outputs for two reasons. First, neighbouring points in an image tend to have similar colours. Second, the two most common types of cones found in the retina have similar spectral tuning curves (Figure 5.1). This means that almost all the information conveyed by a red cone's output is also given by the outputs of nearby green cones, and vice versa.

If the outputs of two cones are similar then sending each of them along a separate channel (neuron) usually represents a waste of capacity. The waste of channel capacity that would result from sending each output along a separate channel can be reduced, and even eliminated, if we can find a way to recode the cone outputs into two new signals which are no longer similar to each other. If the cone outputs contain no noise then one solution consists of recoding them into two new signals which are mutually *independent*, or at least *uncorrelated* (a subtle distinction, discussed in Appendix C), before they are transmitted along their different channels.

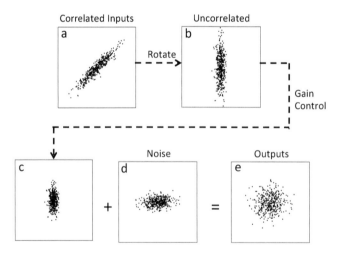

Figure 5.5. A strategy for maximising information. (a) Adjacent sensor outputs x_1 and x_2 are similar, so a scatterplot of x_1 vs x_2 defines a cloud of points along the diagonal. (b) If this cloud is rotated then it produces uncorrelated variables z_1' and z_2'. Each uncorrelated variable (z_1', z_2') is scaled to produce variables z_1, z_2 (c) such that, after noise η_1, η_2 (d) is added, the variables y_1, y_2 are uncorrelated and equivariant (e).

5.5. A Neural Encoding Strategy

In order to encode sensory data efficiently, the brain may adopt a *neural encoding* strategy. To set the scene, consider each input signal to be the combined outputs of two noiseless sensory cells (e.g. photoreceptors) which project to an intermediate neuron (e.g. ganglion cell); this has an output which is a noisy version of its input. The strategy comprises two stages, illustrated in Figure 5.5. First, decorrelation transforms correlated signals into uncorrelated signals. Second, gain control scales each uncorrelated signal so that, after noise has been added, transformed signals are *equivariant* (i.e. they have equal variance). The sensory inputs form a cloud or *joint distribution* of data points, shown in Figure 5.5a, and the two stages of the strategy correspond to two geometric transformations: a rotation followed by scaling along each axis. This represents a recoding of sensory inputs prior to transmission and corresponds to the dashed box in Figure 5.6.

More generally, this strategy can be applied to adjacent signal values, where the signal is defined over different types of domain, including: (1) wavelength, as outputs of sensors sensitive to adjacent parts of the spectrum (e.g. red and green cones, as here); (2) time, as successive outputs of photoreceptors (Chapter 6); and (3) space, as outputs of adjacent photoreceptors (Chapter 7). This strategy is only guaranteed to work if there is no input noise; the more general case of noisy photoreceptors is addressed in Chapters 6 and 7.

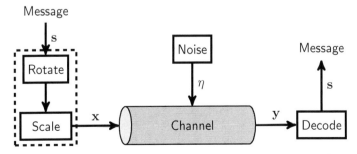

Figure 5.6. Encoding and decoding. The dashed box encapsulates key stages of encoding a message (e.g. stimulus) before transmission. This message comprises parallel components $\mathbf{s} = (s_1, ..., s_m)$, each of which is a variable.

5.6. Encoding Colour

The retinal image in each eye is recorded by 126 million photoreceptors, but neither the image nor the photoreceptors are free of noise. The retinal image is contaminated by stray photons, which degrade the image recorded by photoreceptors. This recording process relies on changes in photosensitive molecules (*rhodopsin* in rods and *photopsin* in cones) and is subject to random temperature-dependent conformational changes which mimic the effects of extra photons. These ghost photons, which occur even in darkness, are called *dark noise* and account for most of the noise in photoreceptor outputs[18].

Each of the 1 million ganglion cells can receive inputs from many photoreceptors, but for simplicity we will consider a single pair of model red and green cones, labelled with subscripts 1 (=red) and 2 (=green), both of which project to a pair of model ganglion cells, as shown in Figure 5.7. Because the cones are adjacent, we can assume that they receive the same light signal s. We also assume that the dark noise (which is unique to each cone) is zero. Thus, the light input to each cone is s, but the effect of this input depends on the cone's tuning function. For example, the light input to the red cone is s, but after being modulated by the red cone's tuning function h_r, the net input is $s_1 = h_r(s)$. The output x_1 of the red cone depends on its transfer

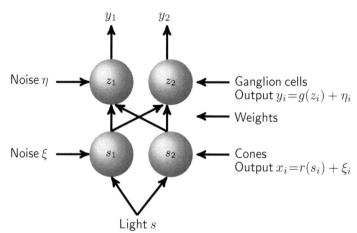

Figure 5.7. Light hitting adjacent red and green cones induces cone outputs (x_1 and x_2) which are combined (via horizontal and bipolar cells) to form the inputs (z_1 and z_2) to two ganglion cells with outputs y_1 and y_2.

(input/output) function f, so that $x_1 = r(s_1) + \xi_1$, where ξ_1 is additive noise in the cone's output. However, for simplicity, we assume the red and green cone transfer functions are linear and that there is no noise in the cone outputs (i.e. $\xi = 0$). Specifically, the outputs of the red and green cones are (Figure 5.7)

$$x_1 = s_1 \quad \text{and} \quad x_2 = s_2. \qquad (5.1)$$

The amount of signal that each cone contributes to each ganglion cell's input depends on the effective strength of their connections. Specifically, the total input to each ganglion cell is a weighted sum of the cone outputs

$$z_1 = ax_1 + bx_2 \quad \text{and} \quad z_2 = cx_1 + dx_2, \qquad (5.2)$$

where each of the letters (a, b, c, d) defines a connection strength or *weight*. We assume the ganglion cell transfer function is linear, so that the output of each ganglion cell is

$$y_1 = z_1 + \eta_1 \quad \text{and} \quad y_2 = z_2 + \eta_2, \qquad (5.3)$$

where η_1 and η_2 are noise in the ganglion cell outputs.

Note that we have named the variables defined above as cone input/output signals, connection weights, and ganglion cell input/output signals because these provide a set of labels that are easy to recognise. However, it should be borne in mind that these refer to *model* cones, weights, and ganglion cells. For simplicity, all variables are assumed to have a Gaussian distribution with a mean of zero.

The rest of this chapter is structured as follows. First, we demonstrate how *sum–difference encoding* can decorrelate cone outputs and how this can maximise information (Section 5.7). We then show how sum–difference encoding is a special case of a more general strategy. This involves measuring the mutual information between cone outputs and ganglion cells (Section 5.8), which allows us to specify the conditions required for connection weights to maximise mutual information (Section 5.9). *Principal component analysis* is explained in Section 5.10. How principal component analysis can be used to maximise the mutual information between cones and ganglion cells is described in Section 5.11. Finally, we consider how this theoretical analysis tallies with the physiology of ganglion cells (Section 5.12).

5.7. Why Aftereffects Occur

Clearly, if the red and green cone signals could be shared out between two ganglion cells then it may be possible to produce ganglion cells with output signals that are uncorrelated. In principle, we could recombine the red and green cone outputs (x_1 and x_2) into two new variables using many different methods, but the simplest method consists of using *linear combinations* of x_1 and x_2. Writing Equations 5.3 in full makes these linear combinations explicit:

$$y_1 = (a \times x_1) + (b \times x_2) + \eta_1 \qquad (5.4)$$
$$y_2 = (c \times x_1) + (d \times x_2) + \eta_2. \qquad (5.5)$$

Crucially, it can be shown that values exist for the weights (a,b,c,d) which guarantee that y_1 and y_2 are uncorrelated.

The similarity between cone outputs is apparent in Figures 5.8a and 5.9a, where the data points lie close to the diagonal. Assuming ganglion

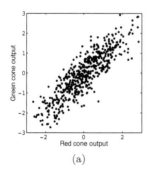

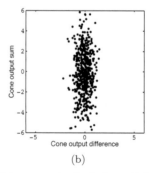

(a) (b)

Figure 5.8. Sum–difference encoding model cone outputs (schematic). (a) Distribution $p(\mathbf{x})$ of correlated red and green cone outputs, x_1 and x_2. (b) Distribution $p(\mathbf{z})$ of uncorrelated ganglion cell inputs, where x_1 and x_2 have been encoded as the sum $z_1 = x_1 + x_2$ and difference $z_2 = x_1 - x_2$.

cell inputs have a mean of zero, the *covariance* between them is

$$\text{cov}(z_1, z_2) \quad = \quad 1/n \sum_{t=1}^{n} z_{1t} \times z_{2t}. \tag{5.6}$$

Expressed in terms of connection strengths (Equation 5.2), this yields

$$\text{cov}(z_1, z_2) \quad \approx \quad 1/n \sum [ax_{1t} + bx_{2t}] \times [cx_{1t} + dx_{2t}].$$

If we define $a=1$, $b=1$, $c=1$, and $d=-1$ then Equations 5.2 yield a sum variable z_1 and a difference variable z_2,

$$z_1 \quad = \quad x_1 + x_2 \quad \text{and} \quad z_2 \quad = \quad x_1 - x_2, \tag{5.7}$$

where a scatterplot of z_1 versus z_2 is shown in Figure 5.8b. Therefore, each term $(z_{1t} \times z_{2t})$ in the summation of Equation 5.6 is the product of a sum and a difference:

$$\text{cov}(z_1, z_2) \quad = \quad 1/n \sum [x_{1t} + x_{2t}] \times [x_{1t} - x_{2t}], \tag{5.8}$$

which comes to

$$\begin{aligned}
\text{cov}(z_1, z_2) \quad &= \quad 1/n \sum x_{1t}^2 - x_{2t}^2 + x_{1t}x_{2t} - x_{1t}x_{2t} \\
&= \quad [\text{var}(x_1) - \text{var}(x_2)] + [\text{cov}(x_1, x_2) - \text{cov}(x_1, x_2)],
\end{aligned}$$

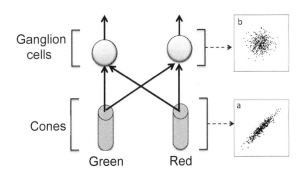

Figure 5.9. Maximising information. (a) The outputs x_1 and x_2 of adjacent red and green cones are similar, so a scatterplot of x_1 vs x_2 defines a cloud of points along the diagonal. (b) Connection weights effectively rotate and rescale cone outputs so that, after noise is added to ganglion cell inputs, ganglion cell outputs are uncorrelated and have equal variances.

so that $\text{cov}(z_1,z_2) = \text{var}(x_1) - \text{var}(x_2)$. Given that the red and green cones have similar tuning functions, their outputs, and therefore their variances, will be about equal (i.e. $\text{var}(x_1) - \text{var}(x_2) \approx 0$), which allows us to conclude that $\text{cov}(z_1,z_2) \approx 0$. Thus, in the simple case considered here, the covariance between the sum z_1 and difference z_2 is about zero, and therefore the correlation is also about zero. In other words, whereas the red and green cone outputs x_1 and x_2 are highly correlated, their sum z_1 and difference z_2 are uncorrelated.

In summary, if we were to send x_1 and x_2 along two different ganglion cell axons then there would be some overlap in the information provided by these two ganglion cells. In contrast, if we send the signals z_1 and z_2 along different axons then there is no such overlap, because the information provided by each axon is unique to that axon.

Scaling. Adjusting the connections between cones and ganglion cells in order to ensure that the inputs to different ganglion cells are uncorrelated has no effect on the amount of information that ganglion cell inputs convey about cone output values; decorrelation simply ensures that the information in each ganglion cell input is not shared by any other ganglion cell.

However, if the amount of noise in the outputs of each ganglion cell is the same then the ratio of signal variance to noise variance will be larger in ganglion cells with larger input variances. This matters because the amount of information conveyed by each ganglion cell's outputs about its inputs (from cones) depends on the relative proportions of signal and noise in a ganglion cell's outputs (see Equation 2.22).

Close examination of the (purely schematic) values in Figure 5.8b reveals that the input z_1 to one ganglion cell has a range of about 12, whereas the input z_2 to the other ganglion cell has a range of about 4. Thus, using weight values of $c = +1$ and $d = -1$ to obtain the difference signal results in very small signal values. Consequently, the difference signal z_2 has very little variance, which makes it vulnerable to the effects of noise.

One way to remedy this is to adjust the weights so that the variance of z_2 is increased. But by how much? In Section 5.9, we will see that information is maximised if the variances of the noisy output signals y_1 and y_2 are the same, as in Figure 5.9b. So if the weights are adjusted such that z_1 and z_2 yield output signals y_1 and y_2 with the same variance then the amount of information will be maximised.

In summary, we (specifically, our brains) do not have to wait until we have decorrelated cone output signals before scaling them to be equivariant. Instead, we calculate the weight values that will automatically provide ganglion cell input signals which are both uncorrelated *and* equivariant; and if the levels of noise in ganglion cell outputs are equivariant then the ganglion cell outputs will also be equivariant.

The sum–difference encoding described above is a particularly simple form of encoding. However, this is really a special case of a more general strategy, described in the next few sections.

5.8. Measuring Mutual Information

So far, we can see from an intuitive perspective why it makes sense to transform cone outputs into new variables (ganglion cell inputs) which are not only uncorrelated but also equivariant. In order to explore this further, we need to know how to measure the mutual information between cones and ganglion cells.

Neurons, Vectors, and Matrices. In geometric terms, the key fact about vectors and matrices is that each vector represents a point located in space, and a matrix moves that point to a different location (Appendix D). When considered over n time steps, the resultant set of n pairs of cone outputs (points) defines the *vector variable*

$$\mathbf{x} \; = \; \begin{pmatrix} x_{11}, & \cdots, & x_{1n} \\ x_{21}, & \cdots, & x_{2n} \end{pmatrix}, \tag{5.9}$$

where each of the $m=2$ rows is a scalar variable. For clarity, the elements of $\mathbf{x}$ can be represented in two equivalent forms. First, as a temporal sequence of n values of the *vector variable*

$$\mathbf{x} \; = \; (\mathbf{x}_1,...,\mathbf{x}_n), \tag{5.10}$$

where the outputs of a pair of red and green cones at time t is represented as the column vector

$$\mathbf{x}_t = \begin{pmatrix} x_{1t} \\ x_{2t} \end{pmatrix}. \tag{5.11}$$

Second, as the temporal sequences of $m=2$ scalar variables

$$\mathbf{x} = \begin{pmatrix} x_1 \\ x_2 \end{pmatrix}, \tag{5.12}$$

where the outputs of the ith cone over n time steps are represented as the scalar variable $x_i = (x_{i1},...,x_{in})$.

Each pair of cone outputs is transformed into the input to a ganglion cell by a pair of weights a and b, represented as a *column matrix*

$$\mathbf{w}_1 = \begin{pmatrix} a \\ b \end{pmatrix}. \tag{5.13}$$

Geometrically, the ganglion cell input is the length of the projection of each data point on to the weight vector, as shown in Figure 5.10. The input to one ganglion cell is defined by the *inner* or *dot product*

$$z_{1t} = \mathbf{w}_1^T \mathbf{x}_t \tag{5.14}$$
$$= ax_{1t} + bx_{2t}, \tag{5.15}$$

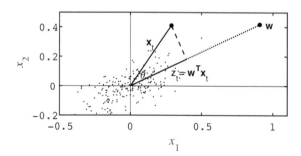

Figure 5.10. The length z_t of the orthogonal projection of a data point $\mathbf{x}_t$ onto a weight vector $\mathbf{w}$ is the inner product $z_t = \mathbf{w}^T \mathbf{x}_t = |\mathbf{w}||\mathbf{x}_t|\cos\theta$.

where T represents the *transpose operator* (see Appendix D). Similarly, for the other ganglion cell, the input is

$$z_{2t} \quad = \quad \mathbf{w}_2^T \mathbf{x}_t \tag{5.16}$$

$$= \quad cx_{1t} + dx_{2t}. \tag{5.17}$$

The input to a pair of ganglion cells at each time step t is one value of the vector variable $\mathbf{z}$,

$$\mathbf{z}_t \quad = \quad \begin{pmatrix} z_{1t} \\ z_{2t} \end{pmatrix}. \tag{5.18}$$

If we define the weight matrix

$$W \quad = \quad \begin{pmatrix} a & b \\ c & d \end{pmatrix} \tag{5.19}$$

$$= \quad \begin{pmatrix} \mathbf{w}_1^T \\ \mathbf{w}_2^T \end{pmatrix}, \tag{5.20}$$

then $\mathbf{z}_t = W\mathbf{x}_t$ and $\mathbf{z} = W\mathbf{x}$. The output of a pair of ganglion cells at each time step t is represented as one value of the vector variable $\mathbf{y}$,

$$\mathbf{y}_t \quad = \quad \begin{pmatrix} y_{1t} \\ y_{2t} \end{pmatrix}. \tag{5.21}$$

If we record the outputs of a pair of ganglion cells over n time steps then the resultant set of n pairs defines the vector variable $\mathbf{y} = (\mathbf{y}_1, ..., \mathbf{y}_n)$. The corresponding pairs of noise values define the noise vector variable

$$\boldsymbol{\eta}_t \quad = \quad \begin{pmatrix} \eta_{1t} \\ \eta_{2t}, \end{pmatrix}. \tag{5.22}$$

In summary, given the definitions above, the ganglion cell outputs are

$$\mathbf{y} \quad = \quad W\mathbf{x} + \boldsymbol{\eta}. \tag{5.23}$$

Not Double-Counting Information. In order to measure the total mutual information between a pair of cones and a pair of ganglion cells it would be tempting (but foolish) to proceed as follows. First, measure the information I_1 that one ganglion cell output conveys about the pair of cone outputs, then measure the information I_2 that the other ganglion cell output conveys about the pair of cone outputs. Finally, assume that the total mutual information is just $I_1 + I_2$. However, if the ganglion cell outputs are correlated then some information I_1 in the output of one ganglion cell must also be part of the information I_2 in the output of the other ganglion cell. So if we added I_1 to I_2 then we would 'double-count' some of the mutual information between the cones and ganglion cells.

A remedy for this double-counting problem would consist of separating out different (i.e. independent) components of the total mutual information. Specifically, if we could somehow find two directions in the ganglion cell output space such that values measured along those directions were independent then any information in one set of values about the cone outputs could not possibly also be part the other set of values. It turns out that we can do just this.

The mutual information between cone outputs $\mathbf{x}$ and ganglion cell outputs $\mathbf{y}$ is

$$I(\mathbf{x},\mathbf{y}) \quad = \quad H(\mathbf{y}) - H(\boldsymbol{\eta}) \text{ bits,} \tag{5.24}$$

which is a multivariate version of the definition of mutual information for scalar variables in Equation 2.15. Thus, we can measure the mutual information $I(\mathbf{x},\mathbf{y})$ as the difference between two entropies: the entropy $H(\mathbf{y})$ of the ganglion cell outputs and the entropy $H(\boldsymbol{\eta})$ of the noise in the ganglion cell outputs.

We begin by measuring the noise entropy $H(\boldsymbol{\eta})$, because this contains lessons for estimating the ganglion cells' output entropy. Crucially, the noise in the output of one ganglion cell is independent of the noise in the output of the other ganglion cell, so that $p(\boldsymbol{\eta})=p(\eta_1) \times p(\eta_2)$, (Equation C.7). Because η_1 and η_2 are independent, the entropy of the joint distribution $p(\boldsymbol{\eta})$ is the sum of entropies of its marginal distributions,

$$H(\boldsymbol{\eta}) \quad = \quad H(\eta_1) + H(\eta_2) \text{ bits.} \tag{5.25}$$

where $H(\eta_1)$ and $H(\eta_2)$ can be evaluated using Equation 2.19.

Just as we hoped to measure the total mutual information by decomposing it along orthogonal directions, we can apply a similar line of reasoning to the measurement of the ganglion cell output entropy $H(\mathbf{y})$. This can be achieved as follows.

A matrix can be used to induce a pure rotation of data. For example, the transformation from Figure 5.8a to Figure 5.8b is a rotation, which is induced by a *rotation matrix* (see Equation 5.26). More importantly, it is always possible to find a matrix A which rotates the ganglion cell outputs $\mathbf{y}$ so that the individual components y_1^R and y_2^R of the rotated data are mutually orthogonal:

$$\mathbf{y}^R \quad = \quad A\mathbf{y}, \tag{5.30}$$

The Rotation Matrix. A matrix projects data points from one location to another. This projection can include a combination of shifts, expansions, and rotations. A rotation matrix simply rotates points around the origin. As an example, the vector $\mathbf{y}_t = (y_{1t}, y_{2t})^T$ defines a point in a two-dimensional space. We can rotate this point by an angle θ with a 2×2 matrix (see Figure 5.10)

$$A \quad = \quad \begin{pmatrix} \cos\theta & -\sin\theta \\ \sin\theta & \cos\theta \end{pmatrix}. \tag{5.26}$$

This projects the point $\mathbf{y}_t$ to a location

$$\mathbf{y}_t^R \quad = \quad A\mathbf{y}_t. \tag{5.27}$$

When written out in full, this becomes

$$y_{1t}^R \quad = \quad y_{1t}\cos\theta - y_{2t}\sin\theta \tag{5.28}$$
$$y_{2t}^R \quad = \quad y_{1t}\sin\theta + y_{2t}\cos\theta. \tag{5.29}$$

---

where $\mathbf{y}^R$ is a rotated version of $\mathbf{y}$, as shown in Figure 5.8b:

$$\mathbf{y}^R = (y_1^R, y_2^R)^T. \tag{5.31}$$

The rotation matrix A can be found using *principal component analysis* (Section 5.10). If the data have a joint Gaussian distribution then this orthogonality ensures that y_1^R and y_2^R are mutually independent, which guarantees that the joint distribution $p(\mathbf{y}^R)$ factorises (Equation C.7):

$$p(\mathbf{y}^R) = p(y_1^R) \times p(y_2^R). \tag{5.32}$$

As was the case with noise, the mutual independence of y_1^R and y_2^R means that the entropy of the joint distribution $p(\mathbf{y}^R)$ is the sum of the entropies of its marginal distributions $p(y_1^R)$ and $p(y_2^R)$,

$$H(\mathbf{y}^R) = H(y_1^R) + H(y_2^R) \text{ bits.} \tag{5.33}$$

Once we have rotated the ganglion cell outputs, we can then measure the entropies of y_1^R and y_2^R using Equation 2.18. But we wanted to know the entropy $H(\mathbf{y})$ of the unrotated data $\mathbf{y}$ in Equation 5.24, not the entropy of the rotated data $\mathbf{y}^R$. So how does this help?

Look at Figure 5.8a (page 72). The distribution of data has a particular spread, which defines its variance, which (in turn) defines its entropy. When we rotate that distribution to produce Figure 5.8b, the spread, and therefore the entropy, remains unchanged. This geometric observation implies that a pure rotation of a distribution has no effect on its entropy; that is, $H(\mathbf{y}) = H(\mathbf{y}^R)$ bits. Substituting this into Equation 5.24 means that we can measure the mutual information as

$$
\begin{aligned}
I(\mathbf{x}, \mathbf{y}) &= H(\mathbf{y}^R) - H(\boldsymbol{\eta}) \tag{5.34}\\
&= [H(y_1^R) + H(y_2^R)] - [H(\eta_1) + H(\eta_2)] \text{ bits.} \tag{5.35}
\end{aligned}
$$

Having decomposed the entropies $H(\mathbf{y})$ and $H(\boldsymbol{\eta})$ into independent components, the entropy of each component can be evaluated using Equation 2.18. Being able to measure the mutual information between cones and ganglion cells is a necessary first step in choosing connection weights which maximise mutual information.

5.9. Maximising Mutual Information

To summarise thus far: given a pair of noiseless cones, each of which is connected to the same pair of ganglion cells (Figure 5.7), the problem is to find a set of connection weight values which maximises the mutual information between cone outputs and ganglion cell outputs. If the total amount of variance (power) of cone outputs is fixed then the problem amounts to finding connection weights which divide up this variance amongst ganglion cell inputs to maximise mutual information.

If we define the weights to be elements of a rotation matrix then the ganglion cell input signals have the same total variance as the cone output signals. Thus, a rotation matrix effectively yields a different variance Z_i^R for each ganglion cell input signal whilst keeping the total variance of the ganglion cell inputs constant:

$$Z_{tot} \quad = \quad \sum_{i=1}^{m} Z_i^R \qquad (5.36)$$

$$= \quad \text{constant.} \qquad (5.37)$$

Next, we measure the mutual information between cone outputs and ganglion cell outputs. In order to avoid double-counting (see Section 5.8), we assume that the joint distribution of cone output signals has been rotated to ensure that the amplitudes of the two ganglion cell inputs vary along mutually orthogonal orientations (as in Figure 5.8) and are therefore uncorrelated. This, in addition to the fact that the noise components of ganglion cell outputs are uncorrelated, ensures that their outputs are also uncorrelated.

The mutual information between cone outputs $\mathbf{x}$ and ganglion cell outputs $\mathbf{y}$ is given in Equation 5.24. Whichever weight values we choose, these cannot affect the noise entropy $H(\boldsymbol{\eta})$. According to Equation 5.24,

$$I(\mathbf{x},\mathbf{y}) \quad \propto \quad H(\mathbf{y}) \text{ bits.} \qquad (5.38)$$

Therefore, in order to maximise mutual information, we need only maximise the entropy of ganglion cell outputs (as in Section 2.6).

In general, the entropy of a Gaussian vector variable $\mathbf{y}^R = (y_1^R,...,y_m^R)^T$ with uncorrelated, iid components $y_1^R,...,y_m^R$ is

$$H(\mathbf{y}) \quad = \quad \frac{1}{2}\log\left[c\prod_{i=1}^{m}\text{var}(y_i^R)\right] \text{ bits,} \qquad (5.39)$$

where the constant $c=(2\pi e)^m$, and $m=2$ here. The variance of each ganglion cell output consists of the sum of the variance Z_i^R of its input z_i plus the variance N_i of the noise η, so that

$$H(\mathbf{y}) \quad = \quad \frac{1}{2}\log\left[c\prod_i(Z_i^R + N_i)\right] \text{ bits.} \qquad (5.40)$$

Substituting Equation 5.40 in Equation 5.38 and ignoring constants,

$$I(\mathbf{x},\mathbf{y}) \quad \propto \quad \log\left[\prod_i(Z_i^R + N_i)\right] \text{ bits.} \qquad (5.41)$$

For convenience, we define

$$k_{Z+N} \quad = \quad \prod_i(Z_i^R + N_i) \text{ bits.} \qquad (5.42)$$

Because the logarithmic function is monotonic, any allocation of Z_i^R values which maximises k_{Z+N} also maximises $\log k_{Z+N}$. Thus, our task is to find weights which yield Z_i^R values such that k_{Z+N} is maximised. Next, we demonstrate that in order to maximise the mutual information $I(\mathbf{x},\mathbf{y})$, subject to the constraint on total ganglion cell input variance (expressed in Equation 5.37), the weights must be adjusted to ensure that $Z_i^R + N_i=$constant for all i.

As noted above, we have no control over the noise variances, so the total noise variance $N_{tot}=\sum_i N_i$ is fixed. Thus, the constraint on total ganglion cell input variance, expressed in Equation 5.37, in combination with a fixed total noise variance, implies a constraint on total ganglion cell output variance, expressed as

$$\text{var}(\mathbf{y}) \quad = \quad \sum_i(Z_i^R + N_i), \qquad (5.43)$$

which can be rewritten as

$$\text{var}(\mathbf{y}) = \sum_i Z_i^R + \sum_i N_i \tag{5.44}$$

$$= Z_{tot} + N_{tot}. \tag{5.45}$$

Given a fixed sum of terms (e.g. $\text{var}(\mathbf{y})$), the product of these terms (e.g. k_{Z+N}) is maximised if all of those terms have the same value. For example, let's assume that the total ganglion cell output variance is fixed at $\text{var}(\mathbf{y}) = (Z_1^R + N_1) + (Z_2^R + N_2) = 6$. Then choosing Z_1^R such that $(Z_1^R + N_1) = 3$ and choosing Z_2^R such that $(Z_2^R + N_2) = 3$ yields $k_{Z+N} = 9$; any other choice of Z_1^R and Z_2^R values yields $k_{Z+N} < 9$.

Accordingly, k_{Z+N}, and therefore $I(\mathbf{x}, \mathbf{y})$, is maximised by setting Z_i^R values such that every term $(Z_i^R + N_i)$ in Equation 5.41 has the same value. This implies that ganglion cell outputs with high noise variance should have low input variance, and vice versa, as in Figure 5.11b. This is known as the *water-filling analogy*[98], because when there are multiple channels, signal power should be allocated to ensure that the signal plus noise power reaches the same level in all channels.

The above result implies that if noise components in the outputs of ganglion cells are iid Gaussian, and if all noise components are

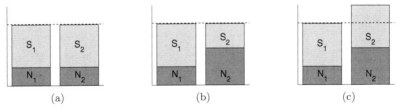

(a)   (b)   (c)

Figure 5.11. Gain control of uncorrelated ganglion cell inputs.
(a) Maximising mutual information yields equivariant ganglion cell outputs $(Z_1 + N_1 = Z_2 + N_2)$, so if noise variables are equivariant $(N_1 = N_2)$ then making ganglion cell inputs equivariant $(Z_1 = Z_2)$ yields equivariant outputs, which therefore maximises mutual information.
(b) If noise variables are not equivariant $(N_1 \neq N_2)$ then different ganglion cell input variances $(Z_1 \neq Z_2)$ are required to yield equivariant ganglion cell outputs (as in Figure 5.5).
(c) If $N_1 \neq N_2$ then making ganglion cell inputs equivariant $(Z_1 = Z_2)$ does not yield equivariant outputs $(Z_1 + N_1 \neq Z_2 + N_2)$ and therefore does not maximise mutual information.

uncorrelated and equivariant, then maximising mutual information transforms the correlated outputs of red and green cones into uncorrelated, equivariant Gaussian ganglion cell inputs, which maximises their output entropy and therefore maximises mutual information. Therefore, given mild constraints on noise, information maximisation can be achieved by the proxy strategy of transforming cone outputs into equivariant, uncorrelated ganglion cell inputs.

However, if the noise terms in different ganglion cells have different variances, then maximising mutual information transforms cone outputs into uncorrelated ganglion cell inputs, also with different variances. These different ganglion cell input variances ensure that ganglion cell outputs are equivariant, which maximises output entropy and therefore maximises mutual information. This scenario is shown in Figure 5.11b, which corresponds to Figure 5.5. However, if we had transformed correlated cone outputs into uncorrelated, equivariant ganglion cell inputs, then ganglion cell outputs would be uncorrelated, but they would not have equal variances (as in Figure 5.11c) and would not therefore maximise mutual information. Thus, if noise terms have *unequal* variances then information maximisation cannot be achieved by the proxy strategy of transforming cone outputs into equivariant, uncorrelated ganglion cell inputs.

In summary, assuming there is a limit on the total amount of cone output power and there is no cone output noise, the necessary and sufficient conditions to maximise the mutual information between cone outputs and ganglion cell outputs are[96]: (1) the ganglion cell outputs are uncorrelated, which is achieved by ensuring that ganglion cell inputs are uncorrelated; and (2) the ganglion cell outputs are equivariant. In Section 5.7, we saw that these conditions can be met using sum–difference encoding. But we can now see that *any* connection weights which satisfy these conditions will maximise the mutual information between cones and ganglion cells. A proof of this result can be found in Plumbley (1993)[92]. Note that the preceding account relies on Theorem 18 in Shannon and Weaver (1949)[105]. A standard method for transforming correlated variables into uncorrelated, equivariant variables is principal component analysis.

5.10. Principal Component Analysis

Principal component analysis (PCA) provides an efficient coding of m correlated variables by transforming them into a set of m uncorrelated *principal components*. If the data is a vector variable $\mathbf{x} = (\mathbf{x}_1, ..., \mathbf{x}_n)$ in which the ith row x_i represents one variable, the inner product of each column in $\mathbf{x}$ with a vector $\mathbf{w}$ effectively extracts a new variable $z = \mathbf{w}^T \mathbf{x}$. For simplicity, we assume $m = 2$ and that the pair of variables x_1 and x_2 represents the output of a red and a green cone, respectively. Accordingly, at a single point in time $\mathbf{x}_t = (x_{t1}, x_{t2})^T$, the new variable has a value $z_t = \mathbf{w}^T \mathbf{x}_t$, as shown in Figure 5.10.

The vector $\mathbf{w}$ defines a direction in the space occupied by $\mathbf{x}$. If we search over all possible directions then we can find a direction for $\mathbf{w}$ which maximises the variance of z. This vector $\mathbf{w}_1 = \mathbf{w}$ is the first *eigenvector*, which has unit length. The variable $z_1 = \mathbf{w}_1^T \mathbf{x}$ is the first *principal component*, and has a variance known as its *eigenvalue*, represented by the letter λ_1 (lambda).

Once we have found the first principal component, we can then remove this from the data $\mathbf{x}$ (using *Gram-Schmidt orthonormalisation*), which yields a modified set of data $\mathbf{x}'$. We repeat the process of searching the space of all possible directions of $\mathbf{w}$ until the extracted signal $z_2 = \mathbf{w}_2^T \mathbf{x}'$ has maximum variance, which defines the second eigenvector $\mathbf{w}_2 = \mathbf{w}$. The variable z_2 is the second principal component, which has an eigenvalue (variance) $\lambda_2 = \text{var}(z_2)$. If $m > 2$ then repeating this process yields m eigenvectors $W = (\mathbf{w}_1, ..., \mathbf{w}_m)$.

Finding the First Principal Component. The projection of each data point $\mathbf{x}_t$ onto $\mathbf{w}_1$ is obtained from the inner product $z_t = \mathbf{w}_1^T \mathbf{x}_t$. Assuming that z has a mean of zero, the variance of z is

$$\text{var}(z) \quad = \quad 1/n \sum_{t=1}^{n} (\mathbf{w}_1^T \mathbf{x}_t)^2, \tag{5.46}$$

which can be written as

$$\text{var}(z) \quad = \quad E[(\mathbf{x}\mathbf{w}_1)^2]. \tag{5.47}$$

Multiplying this out yields

$$\text{var}(z) \quad = \quad \mathbf{w}_1^T \text{E}[\mathbf{xx}^T] \mathbf{w}_1, \tag{5.48}$$

where $\text{E}[\mathbf{xx}^T]$ is the expected value of the inner products $\mathbf{xx}^T$,

$$\text{E}[\mathbf{xx}^T] = \frac{1}{n} \begin{pmatrix} x_{11}, & \cdots, & x_{1n} \\ x_{21}, & \cdots, & x_{2n} \end{pmatrix} \times \begin{pmatrix} x_{11} & x_{12} \\ \vdots & \vdots \\ x_{n1} & x_{n2} \end{pmatrix}, \tag{5.49}$$

which yields a 2×2 *covariance matrix*

$$\mathbb{C}_x \quad = \quad \begin{pmatrix} \text{var}(x_1), & \text{cov}(x_1, x_2) \\ \text{cov}(x_1, x_2), & \text{var}(x_2), \end{pmatrix} \tag{5.50}$$

where $\text{var}(x_1)$ is the variance of red cones, $\text{var}(x_2)$ is the variance of green cones, and $\text{cov}(x_1, x_2) = \text{cov}(x_1, x_2)$ is the covariance between red and green cones. Substituting Equation 5.50 into 5.48 yields

$$\text{var}(z) \quad = \quad \mathbf{w}_1^T \mathbb{C}_x \mathbf{w}_1. \tag{5.51}$$

In fact, the eigenvectors are defined in terms of the data covariance matrix. Specifically, if the direction of a unit vector $\mathbf{w}_1$ is not altered by a matrix $\mathbb{C}_x$ but its elements are scaled by a factor λ_1,

$$\mathbb{C}_x \mathbf{w}_1 \quad = \quad \lambda_1 \mathbf{w}_1, \tag{5.52}$$

then $\mathbf{w}_1$ is an eigenvector of $\mathbb{C}_x$, with eigenvalue λ_1.

Finding All Principal Components. To find all the eigenvectors and eigenvalues, Equation 5.52 is written as $\mathbb{C}_x \mathbf{w}_1 - \lambda_1 \mathbf{w}_1 = 0$, which can be rewritten as $(\mathbb{C}_x - \lambda_1 \mathbf{I}) \mathbf{w}_1 = 0$, where $\mathbf{I}$ is an *identity matrix*. This has nontrivial solutions[99] if $\det(\mathbb{C}_x - \lambda \mathbf{I}) = 0$, where det is the *determinant*[99] of a matrix (see box *Determinants and Entropy*).

PCA can be implemented using biologically plausible learning rules[85], but numerically stable methods, such as *singular value decomposition*, are usually used in practice.

5.11. PCA and Mutual Information

According to Equation 5.23, $\mathbf{y}=W\mathbf{x}+\boldsymbol{\eta}$, so that $I(\mathbf{x},\mathbf{y})=H(\mathbf{y})-H(\boldsymbol{\eta})$ (Equation 5.24). As noted previously, the weights W can affect $H(\mathbf{y})$ but not $H(\boldsymbol{\eta})$, so if we adjust the weights to maximise $H(\mathbf{y})$ then we automatically maximise $I(\mathbf{x},\mathbf{y})$ too. To achieve this, we need to know how to obtain the entropy of $\mathbf{y}$.

Given m Gaussian variables which comprise the vector variable $\mathbf{y}=(y_1,...,y_m)^T$ with covariance matrix $\mathbb{C}_y=\mathrm{E}[\mathbf{y}\mathbf{y}^T]$, the total 'volume' of the distribution of $\mathbf{y}$ values is the multiple integral

$$V(\mathbf{y}) \quad = \quad \int_{\mathbf{y}} \exp[-(1/2)\,\mathbf{y}^T\mathbb{C}_y^{-1}\mathbf{y}]\,d\mathbf{y} \qquad (5.56)$$

$$= \quad [(2\pi)^m \det \mathbb{C}_y]^{1/2}. \qquad (5.57)$$

Recall that the entropy of a single iid variable increases with its total area, which depends on its variance (Equation 2.18). By analogy, the entropy of an iid Gaussian vector variable $\mathbf{y}$ increases with its total

---

Determinants and Entropy. Given a vector-valued variable $\mathbf{x}=(x_1,x_2)^T$, the square root of its determinant $\det \mathbb{C}_x$ is proportional to the area $V(\mathbf{x})$ of the distribution of $\mathbf{x}$ values. For a 2×2 covariance matrix $\mathbb{C}_x = \mathrm{E}[\mathbf{x}\mathbf{x}^T]$, the determinant is

$$\det \mathbb{C}_x \quad = \quad \mathrm{var}(x_1)\mathrm{var}(x_2) - \mathrm{cov}(x_1,x_2)\mathrm{cov}(x_1,x_2) \quad (5.53)$$

$$= \quad \lambda_1\lambda_2, \qquad (5.54)$$

where λ_1 and λ_2 are *eigenvalues*. If $\mathbf{x}$ is rotated until x_1 and x_2 are uncorrelated then $\mathrm{cov}(x_1,x_2)=0$, $\mathrm{var}(x_1)=\lambda_1$, and $\mathrm{var}(x_2)=\lambda_2$, so

$$\det \mathbb{C}_x \quad = \quad \mathrm{var}(x_1)\mathrm{var}(x_2). \qquad (5.55)$$

The entropy of $\mathbf{x}$ is the logarithm of $V(\mathbf{x})$, and if $\mathbf{x}$ is Gaussian then $V(\mathbf{x})=2\pi\sqrt{\det \mathbb{C}_x}$. So $V(\mathbf{x})$ and entropy are invariant with respect to rotations of $\mathbf{x}$.

volume, which depends on its determinant. If we set $m=2$ then

$$
\begin{aligned}
H(\mathbf{y}) &= (1/2)\log\left[(2\pi e)^2 \det\mathbb{C}_y\right] \\
&\propto I(\mathbf{x},\mathbf{y}) \text{ bits.}
\end{aligned}
\tag{5.58}
$$

Following the same line of reasoning as in Section 5.9, if signal power is limited then mutual information is maximised when all ganglion cell outputs are uncorrelated and equivariant.

Given that $\mathbf{y}=\mathbf{z}+\boldsymbol{\eta}$, the covariance matrix of $\mathbf{y}$ is

$$
\begin{aligned}
\mathbb{C}_y &= \mathrm{E}[(\mathbf{z}+\boldsymbol{\eta})(\mathbf{z}+\boldsymbol{\eta})^T] \tag{5.59} \\
&= \mathrm{E}[\mathbf{z}\mathbf{z}^T] + \mathrm{E}[\boldsymbol{\eta}\boldsymbol{\eta}^T] + 2\mathrm{E}[\mathbf{z}\boldsymbol{\eta}^T], \tag{5.60}
\end{aligned}
$$

where $2\mathrm{E}[\mathbf{z}\boldsymbol{\eta}^T]\approx\mathbf{O}$ ($\mathbf{O}$ is a matrix of zeros) because $\boldsymbol{\eta}$ and $\mathbf{z}$ are uncorrelated and where $\mathrm{E}[\mathbf{z}\mathbf{z}^T]=\mathbb{C}_z$ is the covariance matrix of inputs. Given that $\mathbf{z}=W\mathbf{x}$,

$$
\begin{aligned}
\mathbb{C}_y &= \mathrm{E}[W\mathbf{x}(W\mathbf{x})^T] + \mathbb{C}_\eta \tag{5.61} \\
&= W\mathbb{C}_x W^T + \mathbb{C}_\eta \tag{5.62} \\
&= \mathbb{C}_z + \mathbb{C}_\eta. \tag{5.63}
\end{aligned}
$$

Because the noise in different ganglion cell outputs is uncorrelated, the noise covariance matrix $\mathbb{C}_\eta$ is diagonal (i.e. only its diagonal elements are non-zero). Substituting Equation 5.63 into Equation 5.58

$$
I(\mathbf{x},\mathbf{y}) \propto \log[\det\mathbb{C}_z + \mathbb{C}_\eta] \text{ bits.}
\tag{5.64}
$$

PCA of $\mathbf{x}$ provides a matrix W which transforms $\mathbf{x}$ into $\mathbf{z}$, where the components of $\mathbf{z}$ are uncorrelated, so $\mathbb{C}_z$ is diagonal. Therefore, Equation 5.64 involves adding two diagonal matrices, so $\mathbb{C}_y=\mathbb{C}_z + \mathbb{C}_\eta$ is diagonal, which means that ganglion cell outputs are uncorrelated. Recall that we assume each ganglion cell's output variance is the sum of its input variance plus the variance of its noise. As in Section 5.9, if ganglion cell outputs are not only uncorrelated but also equivariant then this maximises $I(\mathbf{x},\mathbf{y})$. Accordingly, if the noise components are not equivariant then the ganglion cell inputs can be rescaled (gain control) so that, when they are added to the ganglion cell noise, the ganglion cell outputs are equivariant, whilst remaining uncorrelated (see Figures 5.5 and 5.11). Similar analyses which include blue cones suggest that efficiency involves the red+green and red–green channels above plus the blue–yellow difference channel observed physiologically[5].

5.12. Evidence for Efficiency

How does the above theoretical analysis tally with the ganglion cells observed in the retina? First, the *parasol ganglion cells*, which comprise 10% of ganglion cells, have an output which is the sum of red and green cone outputs. Second, the *midget ganglion cells*, which comprise 80% of ganglion cells, have an output which is the *difference* between red and green cone outputs in the *fovea*; however, within the *periphery*, each midget retinal ganglion cell has an output which is the *sum* of red and green cone outputs[78]. So both the parasol and midget retinal ganglion cells seem to contribute to the red+green channel, whereas only midget retinal ganglion cells contribute to the red–green (red minus green) channel. These are traditionally labelled as the *luminance* and the *red–green opponent* channels, respectively. These channels are so named because the summed outputs of the red and green cones indicate the overall level of luminance, whereas the difference between red and green cone outputs corresponds to a channel in which red and green act in opposition to each other.

What about the blue–yellow aftereffect mentioned above? Each *bistratified* retinal ganglion cell's output is the *difference between blue cone outputs and the sum of the red and green cone outputs*[78]. Because there is some overlap between the tuning curves of the blue and red/green cones, their outputs are correlated. Without going into details, recoding these as a difference signal ensures that each of the three channels defined above is uncorrelated with the other two. Thus, the three cone outputs can be converted into three combinations, each of which seems to be carried by a different class of ganglion cell.

These results are consistent with predictions by Buchsbaum and Gottschalk (1983)[27] (also Atick et al., 1992[5]). Additionally, principal component analysis (PCA) of natural scenes by Ruderman et al. (1998)[100] predicts the existence of a red+green channel, a red–green channel and a blue–yellow channel. Experimental studies consistent with these results can be found in Brainard et al. (2006)[23]. However, some ganglion cells have complex responses which demand analysis[5;111;126] beyond the scope of this text.

Is Colour Metabolically Efficient or Coding Efficient? If synaptic conductances (between cone and ganglion cells) maximise the collective information rates of ganglion cells then, by definition, these synapses provide coding efficiency. These synapses also provide metabolic efficiency, because if any one of them is changed then this would yield correlated ganglion cell outputs, which represents a waste of ganglion cell energy expenditure. However, individual synapses can have conductances which are metabolically efficient but not coding efficient (see Section 4.11). Assuming that synapses with different conductances remain metabolically efficient, the overall pattern of conductances can still provide efficient coding of ganglion cell outputs (e.g. uncorrelated outputs). Thus, each individual synapse can be metabolically efficient (but not coding efficient) with respect to conductance whilst providing ganglion cell outputs which are both metabolically efficient and coding efficient with respect to the overall pattern of synaptic conductances.

5.13. Summary

We began by considering how, and more importantly why, colour aftereffects occur. We then considered why the correlated outputs from two cones should be encoded into two uncorrelated and equivariant signals. A geometric interpretation of signal spaces suggested that a plausible encoding strategy for achieving this consists of rotation followed by linear scaling of axes (i.e. decorrelation followed by gain control). When considered in the context of retinal machinery, we found that both of these could be achieved simultaneously by adjusting the connections between cones and ganglion cells, and that this can yield metabolic efficiency.

Chapter 6

Encoding Time

> *The present contains nothing more than the past, and what is found in the effect was already in the cause.*
> H Bergson, 1907.

6.1. Introduction

In the previous chapter, we witnessed how the outputs of adjacent red and green cones are correlated and how these outputs can be encoded such that the outputs of different ganglion cells are uncorrelated. By analogy, consecutive outputs of a single photoreceptor are similar and are therefore temporally correlated. Just as similar values in the outputs of two ganglion cells usually represent a waste of coding capacity, so similar values in consecutive outputs of a single ganglion cell usually represent a waste of capacity (see Section 5.5). Accordingly, we consider how temporally correlated photoreceptor outputs can be encoded so that each ganglion cell's outputs are temporally uncorrelated.

6.2. Linear Models

When attempting to model any system, for instance a neuron, we usually begin with a *linear model*, for two reasons. First, most systems behave as if they are approximately linear when considered over a small region of their operating ranges. Second, linear systems are tractable. Every model is defined in terms of key parameters, and if the model is linear then knowing the values of these parameters tells us, in a fairly transparent manner, everything we need to know about the model (and almost everything we need to know about the system).

Within the domain of signal processing, the term linear has at least two interpretations: *static linearity* and *dynamic linearity*. If the response of a system to a single input is proportional to its input then it has a static linearity, otherwise it has a static nonlinearity. For a neuron, outputs are not proportional to inputs, and this nonlinear relationship is defined by the neuron's transfer function (Figure 3.2). If the response to a sinusoidal time-varying input is a sinusoidal output then the system has dynamic linearity, where this linearity provides *sinusoidal fidelity*[109]. For clarity, the term dynamic linearity is unique to this book and is explained formally in the box over the page.

Any system which accepts time-varying signals as input and produces a modified version of those signals as output can be approximated as a *linear model*, also called a *linear filter* or *Wiener kernel*. Of course, if the system is very nonlinear then the approximation will be poor, but we need not concern ourselves with such systems here. We can construct a filter model of a neuron using two very different approaches, summarised in Figure 6.1.

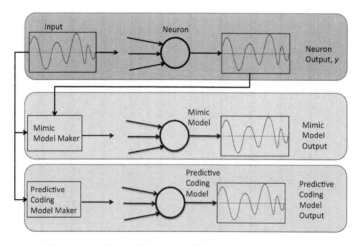

Figure 6.1. Two routes for making a model neuron. The *mimic model* maker uses the measured inputs and outputs of a neuron to estimate the parameter values in a linear filter model of the neuron. The *predictive coding model* maker minimises errors in predicted outputs.

First, we can measure a neuron's inputs and the corresponding outputs and then use these to construct a model. This model is constructed such that, when presented with the neuron's inputs, the model minimises some measure of the differences between the neuron's outputs and the model's outputs. Because this model is based on the measured inputs and outputs of a neuron, let's call this the *mimic model*, and the particular version used here is the *linear–nonlinear Poisson* (LNP) model.

Second, we can measure a neuron's inputs and then use these to construct a model which satisfies certain physical constraints that we think the system should obey. In this case, we think that the system

---

Dynamic Linearity: Linear Time Invariant (LTI) Systems. Consider a system $\mathbb{T}$ which transforms a temporal sequence of inputs $x_1,...,x_n$ into outputs $y_1,...,y_n$. Each input x_t yields an output

$$y_t = \mathbb{T}[x_t].$$

An LTI system passes the tests of *homogeneity* and *additivity*.

Homogeneity. Multiplying x by k also multiplies y by k:

$$ky_t = \mathbb{T}[kx_t].$$

Additivity. If $y_{1t} = \mathbb{T}[x_{1t}]$ and $y_{2t} = \mathbb{T}[x_{2t}]$ then $y_t = y_{1t} + y_{2t}$.

An LTI system is also *time invariant* and obeys the *principle of superposition*.

Time Invariance. The response to an input does not depend on when that input occurs. If $y_t = \mathbb{T}[x_t]$ then $y_{t-\tau} = \mathbb{T}[x_{t-\tau}]$.

The Principle of Superposition. Homogeneity and additivity imply that if two inputs x_1 and x_2 produce the outputs $\mathbb{T}(x_1)$ and $\mathbb{T}(x_2)$ (resp.) then an input $\alpha x_1 + \beta x_2$ yields (see Figure 6.3)

$$y_t = \alpha \mathbb{T}(x_1) + \beta \mathbb{T}(x_2)$$
$$= \mathbb{T}(\alpha x_1 + \beta x_2).$$

---

should have evolved neurons which process as much information as possible for each Joule of energy expended. Specifically, our model is a linear filter which, when presented with the neuron's inputs, encodes those inputs so that it transmits as much information as possible to its outputs. Let's call this general type of model the *predictive coding model*. If we were to construct such a model, based only on the neuron's inputs, would it be a good model of the neuron?

Notice that both the mimic model and the predictive coding model are linear filters, and that both are optimal, but they are optimal with respect to different constraints. The mimic model is optimal with respect to measured inputs and outputs of neurons, whereas the predictive coding model is optimal with respect to the amount of information transmitted from input to output. As will be explained later, the predictive coding model used maximises information throughput only if there is no noise in its inputs.

Despite the fact that these models are optimal with respect to different constraints, the final parameter values obtained with both models are about the same. In other words, a mimic model (designed to emulate the input–output characteristics of a neuron) ends up being similar to a predictive coding model (designed to ensure that its outputs provide as much information as possible about its inputs).

A Plan. The next paragraph gives an overview of methods which will be used to put some flesh on the bare bones of the observations above, so don't worry about new terminology introduced at this stage.

In order to make a mimic model, we first need to find the *impulse response function* of a neuron. A simple method for finding the impulse response function is to find the neuron's *spike-triggered average*. Given that many temporal sensory sequences will trigger a spike, the spike-triggered average is just the stimulus which, on average, elicits a spike; it is really the neuron's favourite input. In practice, neurons have several favourite inputs [94;98;106;107], but here we consider just one.

Statistically speaking, an average is a powerful entity. Under fairly mild conditions, the average of a set of measured values is also the *least-squares estimate* of a true (but unknown) parameter value (i.e. the true mean). For the mimic model, the model's parameters can be estimated as the spike-triggered average. Formally, this model neuron adjusts its parameter values so as to minimise the (squared) differences between neuron inputs and the model's inputs. Under equally mild conditions, the least-squares estimate of each parameter value is a *maximum likelihood estimate* of the true parameter value.

Maximum likelihood estimates have two extremely desirable properties. First, they are *unbiased*, which means that they do not consistently overestimate or underestimate the true parameter value. Second, they have *minimum variance*. This means that if we repeated our set of measurements many times (so that we had many estimates of the true parameter value) then the variance (spread) of estimates around the true parameter value would be as small as possible. For large sets of measurements, this variance approaches a theoretical lower bound known as the *Cramer–Rao bound*.

The reason for pointing out the equivalences between (what may seem like) increasingly rarefied quantities is as follows. The desirable properties of the maximum likelihood estimate are inherited by the least-squares estimate and therefore by the spike-triggered average, which is used to estimate the impulse response function. So when we do something as apparently naive as estimating the impulse response function by taking an average of sensory inputs which elicit a spike (as in Section 6.4), we end up with an estimate which is pretty good, in terms of its basic statistical properties. And even when we do something less naive, like explicitly finding the least-squares estimate of the impulse response function, we end up with an estimate which is also pretty good.

In terms of information theory, if we estimate parameter values by minimising the squared difference between two Gaussian variables (e.g. neuron outputs and model outputs) then this also maximises the mutual information between those variables. So, for Gaussian variables, a least-squares estimate (which is usually a maximum likelihood estimate) also maximises mutual information. Additionally, this applies to any model in which we adjust parameter values in order to minimise the squared difference between two Gaussian variables[49], so it has a wide range of applicability.

As mentioned in Chapter 1, the general idea of neural efficiency can be implemented by a number of different computational methods. However, even though these methods are different, the result of applying any one of them is about the same.

We have chosen to use predictive coding here because it conforms to the broad requirements demanded by neural efficiency and because it is a particularly transparent method. However, in order to provide a benchmark against which to compare predictive coding models, we begin with a particular form of mimic model: the LNP model, which is introduced with a glass of wine.

6.3. Neurons and Wine Glasses

If a wine glass is tapped lightly then it produces a pure tone. Ideally, the sound generated is a sine wave at a single frequency, the wine glass's *resonant frequency*. Conversely, if this pure tone is played back to the wine glass continuously then the glass 'sings along' as it absorbs energy from the surrounding sound. It is as if the wine glass has a favourite frequency, which it emits when tapped, and from which it absorbs energy more readily than any other frequency. If the playback volume is increased then the sympathetic vibrations in the glass increase in amplitude until, at a sufficiently high volume, the glass shatters. Less dramatically, if a moistened finger is moved around the rim then the

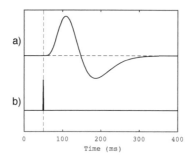

Figure 6.2. If a single impulse (b) could be applied to a model neuron then the response would be a firing rate profile (a), which is the neuron's impulse response function. For a spiking neuron, the impulse response function represents the average firing rate after a stimulus is presented. This response (Equation 6.1) is based on results reported in Adelson and Bergen (1985)[1].

glass emits a sound at its resonant frequency. It is as if the finger acts like a continuous stream of taps, and the result is a continuous tone. What has this to do with neurons?

Every object, including a neuron, has its own set of preferred or resonant frequencies. However, most objects are more complex than a wine glass, so when they are tapped, the resultant sound can have quite a complicated temporal signature: a signature which is uniquely associated with that particular object. Because this signature results from a single tap or impulse, it is called the *impulse response function*.

By analogy with a glass being tapped, a pulse of light on the retina can produce a characteristic temporal profile of firing rates, as shown in Figure 6.2. And just as a finger moving on a glass rim can be considered to be a series of densely packed impulses, so a temporal sequence of luminances on the retina acts like a series of impulses, with an amplitude proportional to the luminance. The output of a visually responsive model neuron is therefore a *linear superposition* of impulse responses, as shown in Figure 6.3.

Of course, rather than measuring the impulse response function of a neuron as a time-varying sound, we measure it as a time-varying voltage or firing rate. And so, for a neuron which responds to luminance (e.g. a ganglion cell), rather than sending it inputs as electrical voltages, we project different time-varying patterns on to the retina. We can then use the neuron's measured inputs and outputs to estimate its impulse

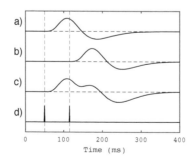

Figure 6.3. If two model neurons receive an impulse at successive times (d) then each neuron would produce a response (a and b). If these two impulses are applied to a linear model then the two responses add to produce the observed superposition of responses in c.

response function. But why do we want to know a neuron's impulse response function? Because the impulse response function of a linear neuron defines its behaviour for all possible inputs.

Crucially, if we know the impulse response function of a linear neuron then we know everything there is to know about that neuron. For example, given a sequence of input values, we can use the impulse response function to estimate its output. More importantly, given a sequence of outputs, the impulse response function can be used to estimate its input. This matters because it is precisely the problem which must be solved by the brain if it is to make sense of the stream of outputs produced by sensory neurons.

A schematic illustration of the impulse response function of a visually responsive neuron is shown in Figure 6.2, where the response to a

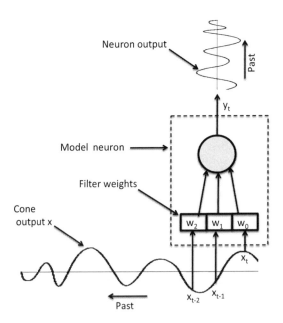

Figure 6.4. The neuron modelled as a linear filter. The neuron responds to a temporal sequence of photoreceptor values x. The neuron input z_t at time t is a weighted average of recent photoreceptor values, where these weights are defined as the elements of a linear filter. This effectively convolves the input sequence with the filter to produce a time-varying firing rate. In practice, continuous signals are sampled at discretised times, as in Equation 6.4.

hypothetical single impulse is described by the equation

$$y_t \quad = \quad \alpha \exp(-\alpha t) \left(\frac{(\alpha t)^5}{5!} - \frac{(\alpha t)^7}{7!} \right) \text{ spikes/s}, \qquad (6.1)$$

where the constant $\alpha{=}0.067$. This particular impulse response function was estimated using psychophysical methods[1] and therefore represents a composite impulse response function from a population of neurons. Nevertheless, the general form of this impulse response function is typical of neurons found in the visual system[101].

6.4. The LNP Model

The basic elements of the linear–nonlinear–Poisson (LNP) model are shown in Figure 6.5. For convenience, we assume that the output of each photoreceptor is identical to its input in this chapter. Consider the time-varying output of a photoreceptor over m time steps up to the present time t,

$$x \quad = \quad x_{t-(m-1)},\dots,x_t, \qquad (6.2)$$

which contributes to the input z_t of a model neuron. This input is a weighted average of recent photoreceptor outputs,

$$z_t \quad = \quad w_0 x_t +, \dots, + w_{m-1} x_{t-(m+1)}, \qquad (6.3)$$

where the m weights specify how much the photoreceptor output at each of m times in the past contributes to the current neuron input

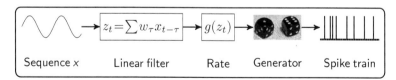

Sequence x Linear filter   Rate   Generator   Spike train

Figure 6.5. The linear–nonlinear–Poisson (LNP) model of a spiking neuron. Given a temporal sequence of input values x, the net input z_t at time t is a linear combination of recent input values. The nonlinear transfer function of a neuron translates z_t into an instantaneous firing rate $g(z_t)$. Within a small interval Δt, the probability of a spike is therefore $g(z_t)\Delta t$.

(see Figure 6.4). Equation 6.3 can be written more succinctly as

$$z_t = \sum_{\tau=0}^{m-1} w_\tau \, x_{t-\tau}, \tag{6.4}$$

where $x_{t-\tau}$ is the photoreceptor output at time $t - \tau$ and w_τ is the weight applied to $x_{t-\tau}$. Note that increasing values of τ refer to filter weights applied to photoreceptor outputs which occurred further back in time, as shown in Figure 6.4.

The m weights are the parameters of a linear filter or Wiener kernel, which is represented as a column vector,

$$\mathbf{w} = (w_0, \ldots, w_{m-1})^T, \tag{6.5}$$

where, as a reminder, T represents the transpose operator. Equation 6.4 defines the *convolution* of the photoreceptor outputs x with the filter $\mathbf{w}$. If we consider all times up to time t then this defines the variable z, which is obtained from the convolution of x with the kernel $\mathbf{w}$, using the *convolution operator* ($\otimes$):

$$z = \mathbf{w} \otimes x. \tag{6.6}$$

If the temporal sequence of m photoreceptor output values up to the present t is represented as a vector variable

$$\mathbf{x}_t = (x_t, \ldots, x_{t-m-1})^T \tag{6.7}$$

then the model neuron input at time t is the inner product

$$z_t = \mathbf{x}_t^T \mathbf{w}, \tag{6.8}$$

where the linear filter $\mathbf{w}$ is defined by m weights in Equation 6.5. The inner product is defined in Equation 6.3 (see Appendix D).

The output y_t of this model neuron at time t is a nonlinear transfer function of its input z_t,

$$y_t = g(z_t). \tag{6.9}$$

The neuron output is a firing rate, which is the number of spikes in a short time interval T, divided by T.

The Spike-Triggered Average and Reverse Correlation. The spike-triggered average is the average of all the temporal stimulus sequences which elicit a spike, as shown in Figure 6.6. This matters because it can be shown that if stimulus values are chosen independently from a Gaussian distribution then the spike-triggered average is a time-reversed version of the impulse response function[33].

In practice, the spike-triggered average is found using a very long sequence of independently chosen Gaussian stimulus values projected onto the retina (for example) while the output of a visually responsive neuron is monitored. Every time we observe a spike, we keep a record $\mathbf{s}_i = (s_{i-m}, \ldots, s_i)$ of the segment of the stimulus sequence for the m time steps which preceded that spike. At the end of the experiment in which the neuron produced, say, 100 spikes, we have a set of 100 stimulus

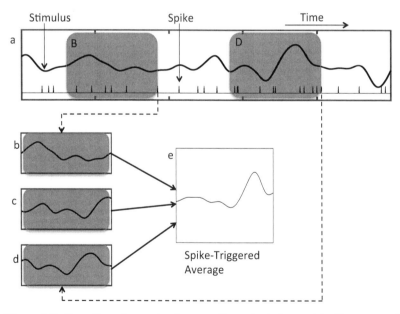

Figure 6.6. Encoding, from stimulus to spike train (schematic). If a temporal sequence of stimulus values (a) is projected on to the retina then a visually responsive neuron produces a spike in response to particular subsequences (e.g. shaded areas B and D). If the subsequence preceding each spike is recorded (e.g. as b and d) then their mean is the *spike-triggered average* (e).

segments; see Figure 6.6. The spike-triggered average is estimated as the mean s_{STA} of these 100 segments. This method is also known as *reverse correlation*. The spike-triggered average has several names, including *reverse correlation function*, *mean effective stimulus*, and *triggered correlation function*.

6.5. Estimating LNP Parameters

We can use least-squares estimation to find values for the weights in the linear filter. First, we define the difference between the neuron's input z_t and the model's input z_t as the noise in the neuron's input,

$$\eta_t \;=\; z_t - \mathsf{z}_t. \tag{6.10}$$

(Notice the subtle difference in typeface used to represent model inputs z and neuron inputs z). When considered over a large number of time points n, a useful measure of the accuracy of a model neuron is the sum of squared errors,

$$E \;=\; \frac{1}{2}\sum_{t=1}^{n}\eta_t^2 \;=\; \frac{1}{2}\sum_{t=1}^{n}(z_t - \mathsf{z}_t)^2. \tag{6.11}$$

The errors in the neuron inputs at all n times are

$$(\eta_1,\ldots,\eta_n) \;=\; (z_1,\ldots,z_n) - (\mathsf{z}_1,\ldots,\mathsf{z}_n), \tag{6.12}$$

where the model inputs are

$$(\mathsf{z}_1,\ldots,\mathsf{z}_n) = (w_0,\ldots,w_{(m-1)}) \begin{pmatrix} x_{1,1}, & \cdots, & x_{1,n} \\ & \vdots & \\ x_{1-m-1}, & \cdots, & x_{n-m-1} \end{pmatrix}, \tag{6.13}$$

where the matrix of photoreceptor outputs can be represented as the vector variable

$$\mathbf{x}_t \;=\; (x_t,\ldots,x_{t-m-1})^T. \tag{6.14}$$

Equivalently, the photoreceptor outputs can be represented as a data matrix with m rows and n columns,

$$X = (\mathbf{x}_1,...,\mathbf{x}_n) \tag{6.15}$$

$$= \begin{pmatrix} x_1, & ..., & x_n \\ \vdots & & \\ x_{1-m-1}, & ..., & x_{n-m-1} \end{pmatrix}. \tag{6.16}$$

Equation 6.13 can now be written more succinctly as

$$z = \mathbf{w}^T X. \tag{6.17}$$

Just to be clear about notation, all of the values in X are from a single photoreceptor output, as shown in Figure 6.7. Specifically, adjacent rows represent successive time indices, and adjacent columns also represent successive time indices. Note that, because successive columns in X are successive m-element segments of x, Equation 6.17 is equivalent to the (discrete time) convolution of x with $\mathbf{w}$, which has the same form as Equation 6.6.

Substituting Equation 6.17 into Equation 6.11,

$$E = (1/2)|z - \mathbf{w}^T X|^2 \tag{6.18}$$

$$= (1/2)(zz^T + \mathbf{w}^T X X^T \mathbf{w} - 2\mathbf{w}^T X z^T), \tag{6.19}$$

where $||$ indicates the length of a vector and where we have treated the scalar variable z as if it were a vector of n elements.

Figure 6.7. Pictorial representation of the data matrix X. Each column represents $m=10$ consecutive output values from a single photoreceptor. For example, the column marked as $\mathbf{x}_3$ is the state of the vector variable $\mathbf{x}$ at the third time step, out of $n=30$ time steps.

The usual method for finding parameter values (e.g. weights) which minimise the value of some function (e.g. E) consists of finding an expression for the slope or derivative with respect to each weight and then using this derivative to find the value of the parameters $\mathbf{w}$ which reduce the value of the slope to zero.

The logic behind this method is that the function E must have a slope of zero at a minimum with respect to $\mathbf{w}$. Turning this argument on its head, if we find a value of $\mathbf{w}$ which makes the slope equal to zero then we automatically obtain a value for $\mathbf{w}$ which corresponds to a minimum of E (of course, it may also correspond to a maximum, but there are ways of checking this).

In this case, the derivative is an m-element vector

$$\nabla E \;=\; \left(\frac{\partial E}{\partial w_0}, \ldots, \frac{\partial E}{\partial w_{(m-1)}} \right)^T, \tag{6.20}$$

where the symbol (∇) *nabla* is standard notation for the gradient operator $\nabla E = dE/d\mathbf{w}$ of a vector and where each element in Equation 6.20 is zero at a minimum of E. From Equation 6.19, the derivative is

$$\nabla E \;=\; (XX^T)\mathbf{w} - Xz^T. \tag{6.21}$$

At a minimum, Equation 6.21 equals zero, so

$$(XX^T)\mathbf{w} \;=\; Xz^T. \tag{6.22}$$

Rearranging this yields the least-squares estimate of the filter weights,

$$\mathbf{w} \;=\; (XX^T)^{-1}Xz^T, \tag{6.23}$$

where $(XX^T)^{-1}$ is the inverse of the matrix (XX^T).

Equation 6.23 would provide an estimate $\mathbf{w}$, but only if we knew the neuron inputs z. In practice, measuring neuron outputs (e.g. firing rates) is much easier than measuring their inputs. In order to circumvent this measurement problem, we will make use of *Bussgang's theorem*. However, in order to establish the necessary notation, we first examine the vector–matrix products in Equation 6.22 in more detail.

First, consider the first term in Equation 6.22, which defines an $m \times m$ covariance matrix

$$\mathbb{C} \;=\; (1/n)XX^T, \tag{6.24}$$

where

$$\mathbb{C} \;=\; \begin{pmatrix} R_{11}, & \cdots, & R_{1m} \\ & \vdots & \\ R_{m1}, & \cdots, & R_{mm} \end{pmatrix}, \tag{6.25}$$

where the ijth element R_{ij} in $\mathbb{C}$ is the covariance (also called correlation) between the ith and jth rows in X (Equation 6.16). Notice that if $n \gg m$ then the law of large numbers allows this to be expressed in terms of expected value:

$$\mathbb{C} \;=\; \mathrm{E}[XX^T]. \tag{6.26}$$

Similarly,

$$\mathbb{Z} \;=\; \mathrm{E}[Xz^T] \tag{6.27}$$
$$=\; (\mathbb{Z}_1, ..., \mathbb{Z}_m)^T \tag{6.28}$$

defines a correlation function, where each element of $\mathbb{Z}$ is the correlation between the photoreceptor output values x in a row of X and the neuron inputs z. The term $\mathbb{Z}$ is sometimes called a *cross-correlation function*, in contrast to the autocorrelation function defined below. Using Equations 6.24 and 6.27, we can rewrite Equation 6.22 as

$$\mathbb{C}\mathbf{w} \;=\; \mathbb{Z}, \tag{6.29}$$

and therefore $\mathbf{w} = \mathbb{C}^{-1}\mathbb{Z}$. It looks as if we need to know the inputs z to obtain $\mathbf{w}$. This is where Bussgang's theorem proves its worth.

Bussgang's theorem. Consider a row of X as a signal x in which values are chosen independently from a Gaussian distribution, and a signal $z = \mathbf{w} \otimes x = \mathbf{w}^T X$, which results from applying the linear filter $\mathbf{w}$ to x. Suppose (as above) we wish to find the cross-correlation function

$\mathbb{Z}$ between x and z. Unfortunately, we only have access to x and y, where $y_t = g(z_t)$ is a nonlinear function of z. Bussgang's theorem states that the cross-correlation function $\mathbb{Z}$ between x and z is proportional to the cross-correlation function $\mathbb{X}$ between x and $y = g(z)$, where each element of $\mathbb{X}$ is the correlation between the values x in a row of X and the neuron outputs y:

$$\mathbb{X} = (\mathbb{X}_1, ..., \mathbb{X}_m)^T \tag{6.30}$$
$$= \mathrm{E}[Xy^T]. \tag{6.31}$$

Specifically, Bussgang's theorem allows us to write

$$\mathrm{E}[Xz^T] = c\mathrm{E}[Xg(z^T)] \tag{6.32}$$
$$= c\mathrm{E}[Xy^T]. \tag{6.33}$$

Substituting Equations 6.27 and 6.31 in Equation 6.33 yields a succinct form of Bussgang's theorem,

$$\mathbb{Z} = c\mathbb{X}. \tag{6.34}$$

Substituting Equation 6.34 in Equation 6.29 yields

$$\mathbb{C}\mathbf{w} = c\mathbb{X}, \tag{6.35}$$

and therefore we can solve for the filter coefficients:

$$\mathbf{w} = c\mathbb{C}^{-1}\mathbb{X}. \tag{6.36}$$

Crucially, neuronal outputs y are relatively easy to measure (unlike neuronal inputs), and we can measure the photoreceptor outputs x, so we have the means to estimate both $\mathbb{C}$ and $\mathbb{X}$ in Equation 6.36.

Even though Equation 6.36 provides a solution (i.e. $\mathbf{w}$), it does not provide much insight. For this, we will take a more circuitous route to the same destination as above. We begin by examining the autocorrelation and cross-correlation functions in more detail here.

The Autocorrelation Function. As stated above, each row and each column in X represents a temporal sequence from a single photoreceptor. It follows that if the rows x_i and x_j are separated by $\tau = (i - j)$ rows then they carry data from two overlapping image sequences, but shifted by τ time steps. So the inner product of the ith row x_i in X with the jth column x_j^T in X^T is effectively x_i multiplied by itself, but shifted by τ time steps:

$$\sum_{t=1}^{n} x_{i,t}\, x_{j,t} \quad = \quad \sum_{t=1}^{n} x_{i,t}\, x_{i,t-\tau}. \tag{6.37}$$

Recall our assumption that all variables have zero mean. If the sequences x_i and x_j are separated by τ time steps then the expected value of the inner product in Equation 6.37 yields the correlation between $x_{i,t}$ and $x_{i,t-\tau}$,

$$R_{ij} \quad = \quad \mathrm{E}[x_i x_j^T] \quad = \quad \mathrm{cov}(x_i, x_j). \tag{6.38}$$

Similarly, if $i = j$ then the expected value of the inner product in Equation 6.37 yields the variance,

$$R_{ii} \quad = \quad \mathrm{E}[x_i x_i^T] \quad = \quad \mathrm{var}(x_i). \tag{6.39}$$

Note that the first row in $\mathbb{C}$ specifies how quickly the correlation between values decreases with temporal distance, which defines the

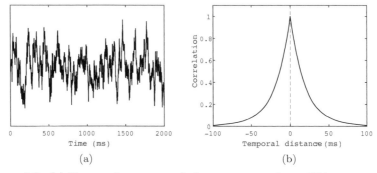

Figure 6.8. (a) Temporal sequence of photoreceptor values. This sequence was obtained by smoothing a white Gaussian signal in order to simulate the statistical structure typical of natural images. (b) Autocorrelation function of x, which reflects the decrease in similarity between nearby signal values.

autocorrelation function of x (Figure 6.8b),

$$\mathbb{R} \quad = \quad (R_{11}, R_{12}, ..., R_{1m})^T. \tag{6.40}$$

The autocorrelation function tells us how quickly the correlation between nearby values diminishes with distance, where distance is measured in terms of temporal proximity in this case. As we shall see, the correlation decreases in natural images, whether distance is measured over time (as here) or space (as in Chapter 7).

The Cross-Correlation Function. Consider the term $E[Xy^T]$ in Equation 6.33. The τth row in X is a sequence x_τ of n photoreceptor values. So the inner product of x_τ with y is the sequence of neuron outputs y multiplied by the photoreceptor values x_τ which contributed to y at a time τ time steps before y. For example, the inner product of the τth row in X with y is

$$E[x_\tau y^T] \quad = \quad 1/n \sum_{t=1}^{n} y_t x_{t-\tau}. \tag{6.41}$$

If x_τ and y have means of zero then $E[x_\tau y^T]$ is the correlation between the outputs y and a time-shifted version of its inputs x_τ, where this

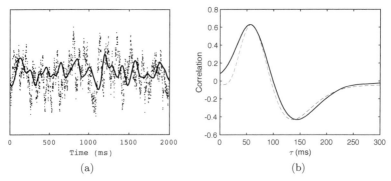

(a)　　　　　　　　　(b)

Figure 6.9. Estimating the impulse response function, or IRF (schematic). (a) Input sequence x (dots, Figure 6.8a), and output sequence y (solid), obtained from the convolution of x with the IRF (dashed curve in b). (b) The cross-correlation function $\mathbb{X}_\tau$ of inputs $x_{t-\tau}$ with outputs y_t is an estimate (solid curve) of the IRF (dashed curve, Equation 6.1).

time shift equals τ time steps,

$$\mathbb{X}_\tau = \mathrm{E}[x_\tau y^T], \tag{6.42}$$

where $\mathbb{X}_\tau$ is the value of cross-correlation function $\mathbb{X}$ at a time shift of τ time steps (Figure 6.9b). The cross-correlation function specifies how the correlation between photoreceptor values (inputs) and model outputs changes with temporal distance between inputs and outputs.

LNP Parameters as the Solution to Simultaneous Equations.
Now, if we write Equation 6.35 out in full,

$$
\begin{array}{ccccc}
R_{11}w_1 + & \ldots & + R_{1m}w_m & = & c\mathbb{X}_1 \\
\vdots & & \vdots & = & \vdots \\
R_{m1}w_1 + & \ldots & + R_{mm}w_m & = & c\mathbb{X}_m,
\end{array}
\tag{6.43}
$$

then we can see that Equation 6.33 represents a set of m simultaneous linear equations with $m+1$ unknowns (i.e. the m filter weights $\mathbf{w}$ plus c). However, c appears in every linear equation, so it simply scales $\mathbf{w}$, and because we are interested in the overall pattern of weights, we have no interest in the value of c. Thus, the solution to this set of simultaneous equations is a set of weights $\mathbf{w}$, which is the least-squares estimate of the optimal filter weights $\mathbf{w}^*$.

Recall that Bussgang's theorem depends on the assumption that input values are Gaussian and independent. In practice, this simplifies matters because it means that if we set up an experiment to estimate $\mathbf{w}$ then we must use a temporal sequence of x values that are Gaussian and independent (recall that we assume photoreceptor outputs are identical to their inputs here). In this case, the correlation between x_t and $x_{t+\tau}$ is zero unless $\tau=0$. Consequently, all off-diagonal elements in $\mathbb{C}$ are zero, and all diagonal elements are equal to the variance $\mathrm{var}(x)$ of photoreceptor output values, so that Equation 6.43 reduces to

$$
\begin{array}{ccccc}
R_{11}w_1 & +0 \ \ldots \ + & 0 & = & c\mathbb{X}_1 \\
\vdots & & \vdots & = & \vdots \\
0 & +0 \ \ldots \ + & R_{mm}w_m & = & c\mathbb{X}_m,
\end{array}
\tag{6.44}
$$

or equivalently,

$$(R_{11}w_1,\ldots,R_{mm}w_m) \;=\; c(\mathbb{X}_1,\ldots,\mathbb{X}_m), \qquad (6.45)$$

where $R_{ii}=\text{var}(x)$, so that $\text{var}(x)\mathbf{w}=c\mathbb{X}$ and therefore

$$\mathbf{w} \;=\; \frac{c}{\text{var}(x)}\mathbb{X}. \qquad (6.46)$$

This means that we can use the cross-correlation function $\mathbb{X}$ as an estimate $\mathbf{w}$ of the impulse response function, as in Figure 6.9.

6.6. The Predictive Coding Model

The laws of physics dictate that an object tends to move continuously over time. This temporal smoothness means that the luminance (brightness) of a single point in the retinal image tends to change smoothly over time, so that the luminance in the recent past is correlated with the luminance now. Such temporal correlations mean that if the recent inputs to a retinal photoreceptor are known then the current input to that photoreceptor could have been predicted, at least to a first approximation (see Figure 6.10). Crucially, if the predicted input to the photoreceptor were to be subtracted from its current input then the photoreceptor's residual input would usually be small, yielding a correspondingly small output. In essence, this is predictive coding. The following account is based on a classic paper by Srinivasan, Laughlin, and Dubs (1982)[112].

Why Predict? In order to reduce the power required by ganglion cells, we can use the photoreceptor output values in the recent past to form a prediction $\hat{x}_t$ of the next output value x_t. Then, rather than sending the measured value x_t at time t, we can send the *error* or *difference* between x_t and the predicted value $\hat{x}_t$,

$$y_t \;=\; x_t - \hat{x}_t. \qquad (6.47)$$

Because x_t is a photoreceptor output, which is estimated as $\hat{x}_t$, we can consider the difference y_t to be noise in the photoreceptor output.

More generally, a neuron that has a prediction $\hat{x}_t$ of its future input x_t effectively also has a prediction of its own future output. Suppose that a neuron tries to generate an output which is the negative of its predicted output. If the input is exactly as predicted then the output the neuron is trying to generate would be cancelled by the effect of the input, and so the output will be zero. In such a neuron, only correctly predicted inputs produce no output. More importantly, only incorrectly predicted inputs (i.e. surprising inputs) produce non-zero outputs.

When considered over a large number n of time steps, a useful measure of the total error in predicted values is

$$E_p \;=\; 1/2\sum_{t=1}^{n}(x_t - \hat{x}_t)^2, \tag{6.48}$$

which can be written as

$$E_p \;=\; 1/2\sum_{t}y_t^2. \tag{6.49}$$

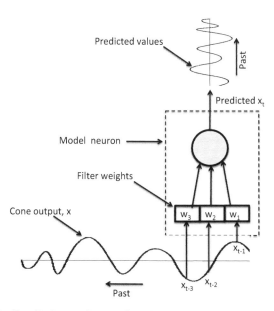

Figure 6.10. Predictive coding. The photoreceptor output x_t at time t is predicted as $\hat{x}_t$ from a linear combination of m previous output values.

Because y represents the neuron's output, and because we will minimise its variance, we also minimise the neuron's output power.

In order to define precisely what we mean by the best prediction, we will reformulate our problem using a vector–matrix notation, and then use this to find the least-squares estimate of the prediction. This section follows the same basic pattern described in Section 6.5.

To keep matters simple, we assume that we wish to predict the state x_t of a single photoreceptor at time t, based on states of the photoreceptor at m times before t and represented as the column vector

$$\mathbf{x}_{t-1} \quad = \quad (x_{t-1},\ldots,x_{t-m})^T. \tag{6.50}$$

We assume that each ganglion cell is modelled as a linear filter, which is connected directly to a single photoreceptor in the retinal image, as shown in Figure 6.10. This linear *prediction filter* is defined by m weights, which are adjustable parameters of the filter

$$\mathbf{w}_p \quad = \quad (w_1,\ldots,w_m)^T, \tag{6.51}$$

where increasing index values indicate weights which are applied to inputs further back in time (Figure 6.10).

The prediction $\hat{x}_t$ of the input x_t at time t is given by a weighted average of previous photoreceptor states,

$$\hat{x}_t \quad = \quad \sum_{\tau=1}^{m} w_\tau x_{t-\tau}, \tag{6.52}$$

which is written more succinctly as the inner product

$$\hat{x}_t \quad = \quad \mathbf{w}_p^T \mathbf{x}_{t-1}, \tag{6.53}$$

as shown in Figure 6.10. The predicted values at all n times are

$$\hat{x} \quad = \quad (\hat{x}_1,\ldots,\hat{x}_n) \tag{6.54}$$

$$= \quad \mathbf{w}_p^T \mathbf{x}_p, \tag{6.55}$$

where $\mathbf{x}_p$ is a vector variable

$$\mathbf{x}_p = (\mathbf{x}_{t-1}, \mathbf{x}_{t-2}, \ldots, \mathbf{x}_{t-n}), \tag{6.56}$$

which can also be represented as a data matrix

$$X_p = \begin{pmatrix} x_{t-1}, & \ldots, & x_{n-1} \\ \vdots & & \\ x_{t-m}, & \ldots, & x_{n-1-m} \end{pmatrix} \tag{6.57}$$

as depicted in Figure 6.11, so that $\hat{x} = \mathbf{w}_p^T X_p$. Notice that the ith column in X_p represents the photoreceptor values for the m time steps before i, which act as input to the filter.

6.7. Estimating Predictive Coding Parameters

Substituting Equation 6.53 into Equation 6.48, the total prediction error can be rewritten as

$$E_p = 1/2 \sum_{t=1}^{n} (x_t - \mathbf{w}_p^T \mathbf{x}_{t-1})^2. \tag{6.58}$$

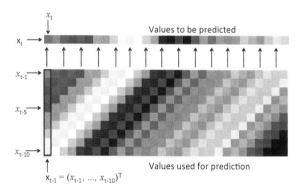

Figure 6.11. Predictive coding based on values in an $m \times n$ (10×30) data matrix X_p (bottom). The photoreceptor output x_t at time t is represented by the tth column in the top row $\mathbf{x}_I = (x_{t-1}, \ldots, x_{t-n})$, which is predicted from the photoreceptor outputs at $m=10$ previous times $\mathbf{x}_{t-1} = (x_{t-1}, \ldots, x_{t-10})^T$, represented by the tth column of the data matrix X_p.

The n photoreceptor values to be predicted define the sequence $x_I = (x_1, \ldots, x_n)$, and the n corresponding predictions of values in x_I are elements of the sequence defined in Equation 6.55. The outputs can now be written as

$$y \quad = \quad x_I - \mathbf{w}_p^T X_p. \tag{6.59}$$

If we consider the neuron outputs y as a vector of n values then we can rewrite Equation 6.58 as

$$E_p \quad = \quad 1/2 \, |x_I - \mathbf{w}_p^T X_p|^2 \tag{6.60}$$

$$= \quad 1/2 \, (x_I x_I^T + \mathbf{w}_p^T X_p X_p{}^T \mathbf{w}_p - 2\mathbf{w}_p^T X_p x_I^T), \tag{6.61}$$

where $||$ indicates vector length. As was the case for the LNP model, the derivative of E_p can be used to find the value of $\mathbf{w}_p$ which sets this derivative to zero. In this case, the derivative of E_p is

$$\nabla E_p \quad = \quad X_p X_p{}^T \mathbf{w}_p - X_p x_I^T. \tag{6.62}$$

At a minimum, this derivative is equal to zero, so

$$X_p X_p{}^T \mathbf{w}_p \quad = \quad X_p x_I^T. \tag{6.63}$$

As in Equations 6.24 to 6.26, this defines a covariance matrix $\mathbb{C} = (1/n) X_p X_p{}^T = E[X_p X_p{}^T]$ and an autocorrelation function $\mathbb{R} = (1/n) X_p x_I^T = E[X_p x_I^T]$, so that

$$\mathbb{C} \mathbf{w}_p \quad = \quad \mathbb{R}. \tag{6.64}$$

Multiplying by $\mathbb{C}^{-1}$ yields

$$\mathbf{w}_p \quad = \quad \mathbb{C}^{-1} \mathbb{R}. \tag{6.65}$$

Thus, $\mathbf{w}_p$ is the least-squares estimate of the optimal prediction filter weights $\mathbf{w}_p^*$. As above (see Equation 6.36), Equation 6.65 provides a solution, but not much insight.

Consider the term $X_p x_I^T$ in Equation 6.63. Each row in X_p is a sequence of n photoreceptor outputs, where the first output in the τth row x_τ is equal to the τth output in the sequence x_I. So the inner product of the τth row of X_p with x_I is x_I multiplied by itself, but shifted by τ time steps, $x_\tau\, x_I^T = x_{I-\tau}\, x_I^T$. The expected value of this inner product yields the correlation between temporal sequences shifted by τ time steps $\mathbb{R}_\tau = \mathrm{E}[x_{I-\tau}\, x_I^T]$. Considered over all time steps, this is the same autocorrelation function as in Equation 6.40: $\mathbb{R} = (R_1, R_2, ..., R_m)^T$. Written out in full, Equation 6.64 represents m simultaneous linear equations with m unknowns (the weights $\mathbf{w}_p$),

$$
\begin{array}{ccccc}
R_{11}w_1 + & ..., & + R_{1m}w_m & = & R_1 \\
\vdots & & \vdots & = & \vdots \\
R_{m1}w_1 + & ... & + R_{mm}w_m & = & R_m.
\end{array}
\tag{6.66}
$$

The solution to these simultaneous equations is a set of weights $\mathbf{w}_p$ (Equation 6.65), which is the least-squares estimate of the optimal prediction filter weights $\mathbf{w}_p^*$.

Prediction Errors Are Uncorrelated. If the ganglion cell outputs y_t are optimal then they must be uncorrelated, which can be shown using proof by contradiction, as in Srinivasan et al. (1982)[112].

Consider the error $y_t = x_t - \hat{x}_t$ in the optimal prediction $\hat{x}_t$ of x_t in relation to the error y_τ at any time $\tau < t$. If y_t were correlated with y_τ then y_τ must contain some information about y_t, in which case it would be possible to use y_τ to improve the prediction $\hat{x}_t$. But $\hat{x}_t$ is, by definition, the optimal prediction of x_t, so it cannot be improved. Thus, if predictions are optimal then the errors (i.e. ganglion cell outputs) at different times must be uncorrelated. In essence, predictive coding minimises the redundancy between consecutive outputs and belongs to class of methods called *redundancy reduction* (Barlow, 1961[15]).

6.8. Evidence for Predictive Coding

This account of predictive coding is based on Srinivasan et al. (1982)[112], where they estimated the impulse response function of visually responsive neurons called *large monopolar cells* (LMC) in the fly. They then compared this LMC impulse response function with the impulse response function estimated using predictive coding. As will be described in Chapter 8, each LMC receives inputs from photoreceptors, so the impulse response function of each LMC depends on the impulse response function of those photoreceptors.

Specifically, Srinivasan et al. estimated the impulse response function of photoreceptors at four different luminance levels (each of which yielded a slightly different photoreceptor impulse response function). The known visual inputs were then filtered using the estimated photoreceptor impulse response functions to estimate photoreceptor outputs, which are the inputs to each LMC. Based on the estimated LMC inputs and outputs, predictive coding (Equation 6.48) was then used to estimate the LMC impulse response function. Because LMCs are non-spiking neurons, the actual LMC impulse response function was measured fairly directly (as a time-varying voltage), by finding the average response to 10 ms flashes of light.

Srinivasan et al. compared the measured LMC impulse response functions with the predictive coding LMC impulse response functions at the four luminance levels mentioned above. Because increasing luminance reduces image noise by a known amount, this effectively tested the predictive coding model at four different signal-to-noise ratios (see Equation 6.66). However, we should note that some of the adaptation to input noise under different luminance conditions is

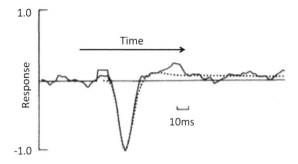

Figure 6.12. Comparison of the impulse response function (solid curve) of a visually responsive neuron (LMC) in the fly with the impulse response function based on predictive coding (dotted curve)[112] at the lowest signal-to-noise ratio (0.6) used. Reproduced with permission.

performed by the photoreceptors, which were not part of the adaptive components of the predictive coding model. A typical result is shown in Figure 6.12, where it can be seen that the match between theory (dotted curve) and observation (solid curve) is impressive.

Just how impressive Figure 6.12 is cannot be overemphasised. The theoretical LMC impulse response function (dotted curve) is based on visual data received by photoreceptors and on the impulse response function of photoreceptors which feed into each LMC. Apparently, the assumption that each LMC uses predictive coding to minimise its output variance is sufficient to predict the precise form of the LMC impulse response function. Notice that the LMC impulse response function is essentially an inverted prediction of future LMC outputs such that the LMC output will be zero if this prediction is correct.

In particular, note that *no free parameters* were adjusted in order to make the predictive coding model fit the LMC impulse response function. Of course, the predictive coding model contains free parameters, but they are adjusted to minimise the errors of predicted inputs and *not* to fit the measured LMC impulse response function. It is therefore surprising that the predictive coding model provides a good fit to the LMC's impulse response function, and we should note that the same arguments apply to van Hateren's (1992) [120;121] more general analysis (see Chapter 7). In contrast, the LNP model described in this chapter contains m free parameters, which are adjusted specifically in order to ensure a match between the impulse response function of a physiological neuron and the LNP model of that neuron. With this in mind, it would be surprising if the LNP did *not* provide a good model of the measured neural impulse response function.

The magnitude of the task achieved by predictive coding and by van Hateren (1992) [120;121] can be appreciated in the context of Freeman Dyson's (1953) recollection regarding model fitting in physics:

> *I remember my friend Johnny von Neumann used to say, 'with four parameters I can fit an elephant, and with five I can make him wiggle his trunk.'*

On a related note, a colleague of mine is fond of saying 'the correct number of free parameters is zero'. To all intents and purposes, the predictive coding model has zero free parameters, but it still fits an elephant, and may even be able to wiggle his trunk.

6.9. Summary

The results presented above provide substantial evidence that sensory neurons act as efficient encoders of the visual world and that one plausible strategy for maximising metabolic efficiency is predictive coding. Indeed, the harsh reality of natural selection suggests that the role of energy is paramount, which implies that metabolic efficiency should be a dominant constraint in determining the temporal structure of neuronal impulse response functions.

The implications of these observations are compelling; neurons are the way that they are because they ensure that their outputs provide as much information as possible about their inputs at the lowest energy cost. On a more abstract note, the mimic (LNP) model of a neuron tells us *how* sensory inputs get transformed into neuronal outputs (i.e. by filtering their inputs), but the predictive coding model tells us *why* sensory inputs get transformed into the particular outputs observed in physiological neurons.

Chapter 7

Encoding Space

*The distortions introduced by the retina seem to be meaningful;
the retina is acting as a filter rejecting unwanted information and
passing useful information.*
H Barlow, 1953.

7.1. Introduction

The problem of encoding space is analogous to the problem of encoding
time, described in the previous chapter. Accordingly, we can follow the
same basic strategy for both time and space. The retinal image is
represented as the output of 126 million photoreceptors (see Chapter
5). As we know from Section 5.2, each retinal ganglion cell collates
the outputs from photoreceptors within a small area of the retina,
which is the ganglion cell's receptive field (Figure 7.1). However, some
photoreceptors effectively have a stronger connection than others, and
the consequent differential weighting given to different photoreceptor
outputs defines the structure of the ganglion cell's receptive field.

Any textbook on human vision will show receptive field structures
which look a bit like a Mexican hat, as shown in Figures 7.4 and 7.6a.
When these were first discovered[62] in the 1950s, it was noticed that
they pick out high contrast edges in images (e.g. Figure 7.6b), which
is why they are often called *edge detectors*. However, it seems likely
that their ability to detect edges is a side-effect of a more fundamental
function regarding information throughput. In order to understand
why this might be true, we need to know about *spatial frequency*.

7.2. Spatial Frequency

Just as a sound can be decomposed into its constituent temporal frequency components, so an image can be decomposed into its *spatial frequency components*. Whereas temporal frequency is measured in terms of complete periods per second, spatial frequency is usually measured as cycles per degree subtended at the eye (Figure 7.2). This decomposition is achieved using Fourier analysis (Sections 2.8 and 7.4).

Low spatial frequencies correspond to widely spaced variations in luminance, and high spatial frequencies correspond to tightly spaced variations in luminance, as shown in Figure 7.3. Just as an audio filter can differentially attenuate certain temporal frequencies, so a spatial filter can attenuate certain spatial frequencies. For example, if a camera lens is smeared with petroleum jelly then the resultant photographs look blurry, because the high spatial frequencies have been massively attenuated; so petroleum jelly acts like a *low-pass filter*.

In computational terms, we can simulate the effects of petroleum jelly using a Gaussian filter, as shown in Figure 7.5b. This blurred image was obtained using the Gaussian filter or kernel shown in Figure 7.5a. All of the filters considered here have radially symmetric (i.e. circular) weights, which means that the value of a weight depends only on the distance d from the filter's centre. For the Gaussian filter $\mathbf{w}$ (Figure

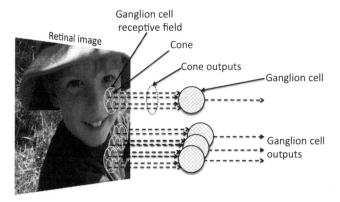

Figure 7.1. The retinal image activates cones, where each cone projects to one or more ganglion cells (via bipolar and horizontal cells, not shown). Here, each ganglion cell receptive field has four cones, but this can vary between one and (more typically) 100–1000 cones[114].

7.5a), the value of the filter weighting at a point (a,b) (which is a distance $d=\sqrt{a^2+b^2}$ from the centre of the filter) is

$$\mathbf{w}_{ab} \quad = \quad c\,e^{-(a^2+b^2)/(2v)}, \tag{7.1}$$

where v is the variance of the Gaussian, and the constant $c=1/2\pi v$.

Consider a filter which is centred at a point i,j in the image, where i is its location along the horizontal axis and j is its location along the vertical axis. This filter gathers its inputs from an array of photoreceptors, where the effective connection strength between the filter and each photoreceptor defines the receptive field of the filter, as shown in Figure 5.2. These different connection strengths mean that the filter output is a weighted average of photoreceptor outputs within its receptive field,

$$z_{ab} \quad = \quad \sum_{i=a-k}^{a+k}\sum_{j=b-k}^{b+k} \mathbf{w}_{ab}\,x_{a+i,b+j}, \tag{7.2}$$

where k defines the outer limits of the receptive field, so that $\mathbf{w}$ has a total of $(2k+1)^2$ weights (this defines a square receptive field, which is a trivial side-effect of the notation used here). If the image consists of a square array of $n=N \times N$ photoreceptors, and if we place the centre of one filter over each photoreceptor, then (using Equation 7.2) the array of filter outputs is represented as the variable $z=(z_1,...,z_n)$. This can

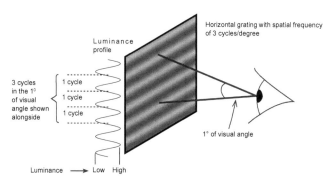

Figure 7.2. Grating with a spatial frequency of 3 cycles/degree. This means that 3 complete cycles of sinusoidal luminance occur in each degree of visual angle. Reproduced with permission from Frisby and Stone (2010)[45].

be written using the convolution operator (see Section 6.4, p100) as

$$z \quad = \quad \mathbf{w} \otimes x, \tag{7.3}$$

where $\mathbf{w}$ is a two-dimensional weight matrix of filter values defined in Equation 7.1, as shown in Figure 7.5a, where each value in z is obtained from Equation 7.2. As we shall see, it usually makes little biological sense to pack filters as densely as we have here (i.e. one filter per photoreceptor), but this is effectively what happens when we convolve an image with a filter using a computer.

Ganglion Cells as Spatial Filters. We can interpret the filter $\mathbf{w}$ as the receptive field of a ganglion cell, such that $\mathbf{w}$ represents the effective connection strengths between photoreceptors and the ganglion cell. The output x of each photoreceptor depends on the retinal image s plus noise ξ,

$$x \quad = \quad s + \xi, \tag{7.4}$$

where we assume that the photoreceptor transfer function is linear. An array of photoreceptors has outputs x, which are processed by the filter $\mathbf{w}$ (receptive field) of a ganglion cell, so that the ganglion cell's input is given by Equation 7.3, and its output is

$$y \quad = \quad g(z) + \eta, \tag{7.5}$$

where η is the noise in the output of the ganglion cell.

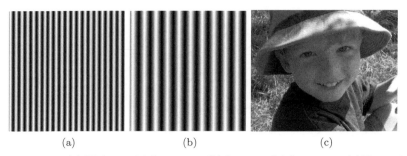

(a)   (b)   (c)

Figure 7.3. (a) High spatial frequency. (b) Low spatial frequency. (c) Natural images contain a mixture of spatial frequencies.

In principle, we could take account of both photoreceptor noise ξ and ganglion cell noise[93;120] η. However, we are mainly interested in changes associated with varying luminance, which affects photoreceptor noise ξ. Accordingly, (for the present) we assume there is no ganglion cell noise, i.e. $\eta = 0$. We assume the ganglion cell transfer function g is linear, so that the ganglion cell output is

$$ y \;\; = \;\; \mathbf{w} \otimes (s + \xi). \tag{7.6} $$

On-Centre and Off-Centre Ganglion Cells. As mentioned in the Introduction, the structure of a typical ganglion cell receptive field resembles a Mexican hat, as shown in Figures 7.4 (left) and 7.6a. This means that a spot of light within the central region increases ganglion cell firing rate, whereas light in the surrounding annulus reduces the firing rate. This type of ganglion cell is called an *on-centre cell*. So the image on the retina resembles Figure 7.3c, but the 'image' received by the brain looks more like Figure 7.6b.

However, light in the surround of an on-centre cell's receptive field reduces the baseline firing rate (typically 1–2 spikes/s) to about zero spikes/s. This means that on-centre ganglion cells can signal contrasts from zero upwards but cannot signal negative contrasts (the left and right sides of Figure 7.4 also depict positive and negative contrast, respectively). The full range of positive and negative image contrasts requires a complementary population of *off-centre cells*, which can signal contrasts from zero downwards but cannot signal positive

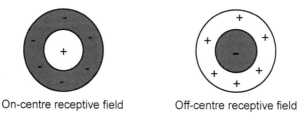

On-centre receptive field   Off-centre receptive field

Figure 7.4. Schematic representation of on-centre ganglion cell receptive field (left), more accurately portrayed in Figure 7.6a, and off-centre ganglion cell receptive field (right). Plus symbols indicate regions where light increases ganglion cell output, and minus symbols indicate regions where light decreases output.

contrasts. Thus, on-centre cells signal the presence of positive contrasts, and off-centre cells signal the presence of negative contrasts. If their outputs were to be combined in a hypothetical composite on–off ganglion cell then this composite cell would be able to signal both positive and negative contrasts. This hypothetical on–off ganglion cell has an intriguing, and potentially useful, side-effect.

The output of a ganglion cell is a nonlinear (transfer) function of its input. However, if the inputs to a composite on–off ganglion cell are obtained by subtracting on-centre from off-centre ganglion cell outputs then those inputs are approximately linearly related to image contrasts[40;116]. This is a spatial version of opponent processing of cone outputs (Chapter 5). For simplicity, we assume that ganglion cells are composite on–off ganglion cells, which have both positive and negative outputs, with Mexican hat receptive fields like Figure 7.6a.

Just as we can simulate the blurring filter with a Gaussian function, so we can simulate the typical Mexican hat filter (Figure 7.6a) with the difference between two Gaussian functions. This *difference-of-Gaussian* (DoG) filter consists of a narrow Gaussian function which provides the excitatory centre minus a wide Gaussian function which provides the inhibitory surround. For the DoG filter $\mathbf{w}$ (Figure 7.6a), the value of the filter weighting at a distance $d = \sqrt{a^2 + b^2}$ from the centre of the filter is

$$\mathbf{w}_{ab} \quad = \quad c_E e^{-d^2/(2v_E)} \;-\; c_I e^{-d^2/(2v_I)}, \qquad (7.7)$$

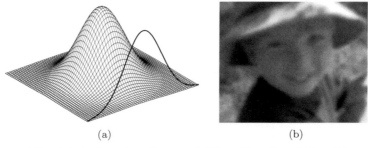

(a) (b)

Figure 7.5. (a) A Gaussian (low-pass) filter (Equation 7.1), with profile shown as a black curve. (b) When convolved with Figure 7.3c, this filter attenuates high spatial frequencies. The filter used here and in Figure 7.6 is about 2 mm × 2 mm.

where v_E is the variance of the excitatory centre and v_I is the variance of the inhibitory surround (a typical value for the ratio $v_I/v_E \approx 1.6$). The normalisation constants are $c_E = 1/(2v_E\pi)$ and $c_I = 1/(2v_I\pi)$.

7.3. Do Ganglion Cells Decorrelate Images?

Before we consider the more formal aspects of how ganglion cells can maximise their information throughput, we will perform a simple test. If ganglion cells act as efficient communication channels then we should expect their outputs to be less correlated than pixel (photoreceptor) values (at least under high-luminance conditions).

Accordingly, we take an ordinary image (Figure 7.3c) and measure the correlation between every pair of adjacent pixels. Then we measure the correlation between pixels that are two pixels apart, then three, and so on, up to a distance of 10 pixels. A scatter plot of pairs of pixel values which are 10 pixels apart is shown in Figure 7.7a. This reveals that most pairs are fairly similar, and they have a mean correlation of about 0.7. So even at this distance, each pixel provides substantial information about its neighbours (about half a bit). If we plot the measured inter-pixel correlation at each distance then the result is the spatial autocorrelation function of the image, as shown in Figure 7.7b.

Next, we convolve the image with a filter which approximates a typical ganglion cell receptive field, as in Figure 7.6a. The result is a convolution image, Figure 7.6b, in which each grey level is proportional to the output of a ganglion cell centred at the same point in the original

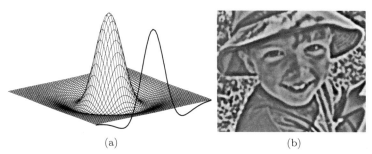

(a)   (b)

Figure 7.6. (a) A DoG filter (Equation 7.7), with profile shown as a black curve. (b) When convolved with Figure 7.3c, this (band-pass) filter attenuates high and low spatial frequencies.

(unfiltered) image, Figure 7.3c. Now we measure the correlations between ganglion cell outputs separated by different distances (i.e. in Figure 7.3c). The result is a scatterplot of ganglion cell outputs and a ganglion cell autocorrelation function, as shown in Figure 7.8. In contrast to the image autocorrelation function, which falls slowly from a value of 1 to 0.7, the corresponding ganglion cell autocorrelation function falls rapidly from 1 to about zero at a distance of 10 image pixels. Thus, the ganglion cells have effectively decorrelated the image.

Of course, this assumes that ganglion cells are packed as densely as photoreceptors, which would mean that adjacent cells would have highly correlated outputs. This, in itself, tells us that it probably makes sense to have ganglion cells separated by a distance which ensures that their outputs are uncorrelated. In this schematic example, that distance would be about 10 photoreceptors, because ganglion cells separated by 10 pixels have a correlation of zero (see Section 7.11). This is clearly not a rigorous test, but it does suggest that ganglion cell outputs are more uncorrelated than corresponding photoreceptor outputs.

Evidence that ganglion cell outputs are uncorrelated was obtained by Nirenberg et al. (2001)[82]. They projected images onto the retina and measured the amount of information that could be recovered about those images from the outputs of ganglion cells. They then calculated how much of this mutual information would be lost if the correlations between ganglion cells were ignored and found the answer to be about

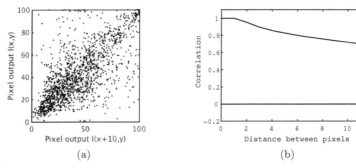

Figure 7.7. (a) Scatter plot of pixel grey-level pairs separated by 10 pixels in Figure 7.3c. (b) Pixel autocorrelation function (i.e. how the correlation between pixel grey levels decreases as the distance between pixels increases).

10%. So almost all (90%) of the information carried by each ganglion cell is unique to that ganglion cell, which implies that ganglion cell outputs are largely independent.

Pitkow and Meister (2012)[91] measured the correlation between pairs of ganglion cell outputs at different inter-cell distances in the retina and compared this to the correlation between corresponding pairs of image pixel outputs (which we can treat as photoreceptor outputs). Their results, shown in Figure 7.9, are qualitatively similar to Figures 7.7 and 7.8 (but they emphasise that decorrelation is due to a combination of receptive field, nonlinear transfer functions, and noise). Taken together, these studies suggest that the retinal image is encoded to reduce correlations between ganglion cell outputs, which reduces redundancy in ganglion cell outputs.

7.4. Optimal Receptive Fields: Overview

So far, we have found evidence that ganglion cell outputs are less correlated than corresponding photoreceptor outputs, which is consistent with efficient use of ganglion cells as communication channels. However, even though this was not explicitly stated, this evidence was obtained under high-luminance conditions. In this section, we explore information in more detail, and we will find that decorrelation is only part of the story. In essence, under high-luminance conditions, information throughput is maximised by the decorrelating

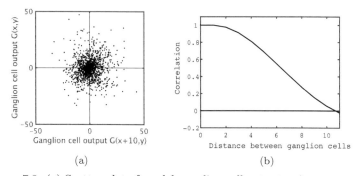

(a)   (b)

Figure 7.8. (a) Scatter plot of model ganglion cell output pairs separated by 10 pixels in Figure 7.6c. (b) Ganglion cell autocorrelation function.

Mexican hat receptive field (Figure 7.6). However, under low-luminance conditions, information throughput is maximised by a receptive field that implements local averaging (Figure 7.5), for which ganglion cell outputs are *more correlated* than corresponding photoreceptor outputs.

Ganglion Cells and Noise. The number of photons reaching the retina decreases as light levels fall. However, the amount of noise in photoreceptor outputs is fairly constant because it is dominated by spontaneous thermal activity (see Section 5.6). Thus, as light levels fall, the *proportion* of noise in photoreceptor outputs increases, which decreases the signal-to-noise ratio.

Armed with this knowledge, we can now ask two key questions. (1) Given that falling light levels reduce the signal-to-noise ratio of photoreceptors, what is the optimal receptive field structure at each light level? (2) Is the receptive field structure found in the eye at each light level similar to this optimal structure? In order to answer these questions, we need to know more about the Fourier analysis of images.

Fourier analysis is usually applied to time-varying signals (where frequency is measured in cycles/s), but it can also be applied to images (where frequency is measured in cycles/degree). Whereas time is one-dimensional, an image is two-dimensional, so each Fourier component of an image has both a frequency and an orientation specified in image coordinates. For example, the gratings in Figures 7.3a and b have

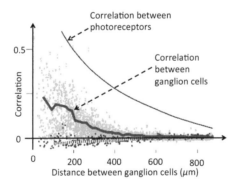

Figure 7.9. The correlation between ganglion cell outputs decreases with retinal inter-cell distance in larval tiger salamanders. Each point represents the correlation between two ganglion cells, and the solid line represents the median. The thin curve is the correlation between photoreceptor outputs. Reproduced with permission from Pitkow and Meister (2012)[91].

different frequencies but the same (vertical) orientation. However, in order to keep notation uncluttered, we will treat Fourier components as if we had averaged over all orientations within an image.

A ganglion cell's receptive field acts as an image filter, which allows some spatial frequencies to affect its output more than others. By altering the weights between the ganglion cell and the photoreceptors in its receptive field, a ganglion cell can modify the extent to which different spatial frequencies affect its output (see Figure 7.10). Thus, the connection weights $\mathbf{w}$ between photoreceptors and a ganglion cell define a filter that assigns a gain to each spatial frequency f.

Most of the power in images of natural scenes is associated with big structures rather than small details. More precisely, the power S_f of a Fourier component with a frequency of f cycles/degree is

$$S(f) \quad = \quad \frac{c_S}{f^2}, \tag{7.8}$$

where $c_S = 10^{-4}$ (as in van Hateren, 1992[120]), so that signal power falls very rapidly with frequency[6], as shown in Figure 7.11a. In contrast, noise usually has a *white* (i.e. flat) power spectrum[7].

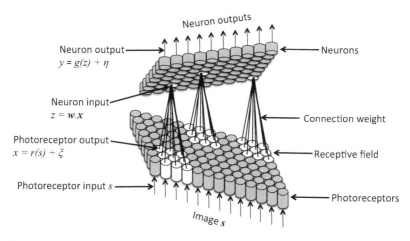

Figure 7.10. Generic neural architecture for visual processing. Light reaches the photoreceptors first in invertebrates, as shown here. In vertebrates, these layers are reversed and light passes through neural layers (e.g. ganglion cells) to reach the photoreceptors.

Because low frequencies dominate the power spectrum of natural images, and because noise is white, the 'image' of photoreceptor outputs has a power spectrum which has large power at very low spatial frequencies, but most of the power at very high frequencies is due to noise. This means that any attempt to equalise signal plus photoreceptor noise power across all frequencies has the effect of increasing the amplitude of noise in high frequency components. Consequently, just whitening signal plus noise can decrease mutual information. This is why models[7] which only whiten their outputs (but do not explicitly maximise mutual information) remove high frequencies before whitening is applied.

To some extent, this seems to be the strategy adopted by the visual system, because the relatively poor optics of the eye[7] effectively attenuate high spatial frequencies (Figure 7.11b). However, the problem of transmitting information under both high- and low-luminance conditions remains, as discussed in Sections 7.7 and 7.8.

7.5. Receptive Fields and Information

Recall that we wish to find the mutual information between the image s and the neuron output y. In order to do this, we need to estimate the entropy of the signal and noise. However, whereas the signal

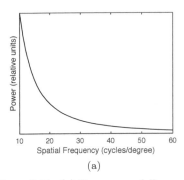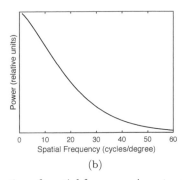

(a) (b)

Figure 7.11. (a) How power falls as a function of spatial frequency in natural images (Equation 7.8). For display purposes, only frequencies up to 60 cycles/degree are shown. (b) The *modulation transfer function* of the eye attenuates high spatial frequencies[7].

entropy is expressed in terms of the photoreceptor input, the noise is expressed variously in terms of photoreceptor input, photoreceptor output, neuron input, and neuron output. In essence, we need to express all of the signal and noise entropies in the same space; that is, in terms of the input or in terms of the output. We begin by expressing all entropies in terms of the output space. For convenience, we assume all variables are Gaussian.

Consider an image that has power $S(f)$ at spatial frequency f. If the *photoreceptor filter* assigns a gain $\sqrt{R(f)}$ and the *neural filter* assigns a gain $\sqrt{G(f)}$ then the signal power of frequency f at the output is

$$S_{op}(f) \quad = \quad G(f)R(f)S(f), \tag{7.9}$$

where the squared gain of a filter (e.g. $R(f)$) at frequency f is referred to as the filter power. Similarly, the total noise power of frequency f at the output is

$$N_{op}(f) \quad = \quad G(f)R(f)N_s(f) + G(f)N_\varepsilon(f) + N_\eta(f). \tag{7.10}$$

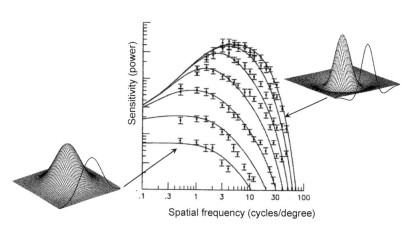

Figure 7.12. Predicted ganglion cell receptive field characteristics (solid curves)[7], under low-luminance conditions (lower curves) and high-luminance conditions (upper curves). Data points depict human sensitivity under different lighting conditions. Under low-luminance conditions, the predicted ganglion cell receptive field (shown on left) is a low-pass filter, but under high-luminance conditions it is a band-pass filter (shown on right). Graph reproduced with permission from Atick and Redlich (1992)[7].

For convenience, we assume that photoreceptor input noise $N_s(f)$ can be absorbed into the photoreceptor output noise $N_\varepsilon(f)$, and we therefore assume $N_s(f)=0$ from now on, so that

$$N_{op}(f) = G(f)N_\varepsilon(f) + N_\eta(f). \qquad (7.11)$$

The total output power at frequency f is therefore

$$V_y(f) = G(f)R(f)S(f) + G(f)N_\varepsilon(f) + N_\eta(f) \qquad (7.12)$$
$$= S_{op}(f) + N_{op}(f). \qquad (7.13)$$

If the input image s and the neural output y are Gaussian then (following Equation 2.28) the mutual information between them is

$$I(s,y) = \int_{f=0}^{W} \log\left(1 + \frac{S_{op}(f)}{N_{op}(f)}\right) df \text{ bits}, \qquad (7.14)$$

which corresponds to R_{info}. Substituting Equations 7.9 and 7.13 in Equation 7.14,

$$I(s,y) = \int_f \log\left(1 + \frac{G(f)R(f)S(f)}{G(f)N_\varepsilon(f) + N_\eta(f)}\right) df \text{ bits.} \qquad (7.15)$$

Rather than expressing entropies in terms of output space, we can express them in terms of input space. Clearly, the signal variance of frequency f in the input space is $S(f)$. The process of expressing noise components in terms of input space is called *referring the noise to the input*[98]. In essence, this allows us to treat noise anywhere in the system as if it originated at the input. So we would like to find the *effective noise* variance $N_{eff}(f)$ of frequency f at the input, such that

$$N_{op}(f) = G(f)R(f)N_{eff}(f). \qquad (7.16)$$

Re-arranging, and making use of Equation 7.11 yields

$$N_{eff}(f) = \frac{N_\varepsilon(f)}{R(f)} + \frac{N_\eta(f)}{G(f)R(f)}. \qquad (7.17)$$

Substituting Equations 7.9 and 7.16 into Equation 7.14,

$$I(s,y) \quad = \quad \int_f \log\left(1 + \frac{S(f)}{N_{eff}(f)}\right) df \text{ bits.} \qquad (7.18)$$

Whether we express variables in terms of input or output space, it looks as if we need to know the values of the parameters of photoreceptor and neural filters. However, we can also proceed by estimating the parameters of the overall photoreceptor–neuron system, as follows.

7.6. Measuring Mutual Information

Our overall goal is to evaluate the mutual information $I(s,y)$. In principle, we could estimate mutual information by first estimating the individual filter and input and output noise characteristics of photoreceptors and neurons in Equation 7.15. However, in practice it is simpler to estimate mutual information from the overall photoreceptor inputs and neuron outputs, using either Equation 7.14 or Equation 7.18; for reasons explained below, we begin with Equation 7.18.

This section and Section 7.7 are based on a paper by de Ruyter van Steveninck and Laughlin (1996) [34], which was one of the first papers to measure information at different stages in the visual system of a fly.

Under laboratory conditions, the stimulus s (and therefore the signal variance $S(f)$) is controlled by the experimenter, so the only unknown is the effective noise variance $N_{eff}(f)$, which can be estimated, as follows. The variance $S_{op}(f)$ of the filtered signal in the output can be estimated as the mean response to repeated presentations of the same temporal stimulus, as shown in Figure 7.13. The overall gain $\sqrt{F(f)}$ of the photoreceptor–neuron system at frequency f can be obtained from the known variance $S(f)$ of the input signal and the variance $S_{op}(f)$ of the neuron output, which defines the *system filter*

$$F(f) \quad = \quad \frac{S_{op}(f)}{S(f)}, \qquad (7.19)$$

where $F(f)=G(f)R(f)$. The squared system gain $F(f)$ transforms the noise variance $N_{op}(f)$ in the output into the effective noise variance at the input,

$$N_{eff}(f) = \frac{N_{op}(f)}{F(f)}. \tag{7.20}$$

However, this assumes that the output noise variance $N_{op}(f)$ is known. In fact, $N_{op}(f)$ can be estimated as follows.

Repeated presentations of the same stimulus yields a set of neuron responses, where the mean response is assumed to represent the response to the stimulus signal. Accordingly, the difference between the mean response and the response on an individual trial represents the noise on that trial, as shown in Figure 7.13. A Fourier transform of each noise response yields an estimate of the trial-specific noise variance at each frequency. When these variances are averaged over trials, the result is an estimate of the noise variance $N_{op}(f)$ at each frequency.

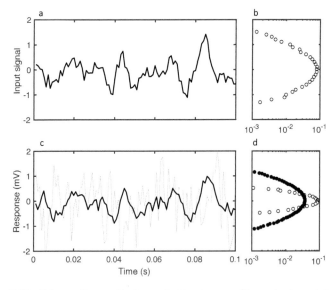

Figure 7.13. Schematic results from de Ruyter van Steveninck and Laughlin (1996)[34]. (a) Stimulus contrast s varies over time. (b) Distribution of contrast values (dots) is approximately Gaussian. Repeated presentations of the stimulus yield a slightly different response on each trial. (c) Exemplar response to one presentation (faint curve), and mean response (black curve). The difference between the mean response and the response on each presentation represents noise. (d) Distribution of mean responses (filled circles) and noise responses (open circles). Adapted from Schultz (2007)[102].

Given values for $S_{op}(f)$ and $N_{op}(f)$, we could also estimate mutual information from Equation 7.14.

Once estimates of $S(f)$ and $N_{eff}(f)$ were obtained by de Ruyter van Steveninck and Laughlin (1996)[34], they were substituted into Equation 7.18 to estimate the information rate, which was found to be 1,150 bits/s for an LMC neuron. A version of the water-filling method[30] was used to estimate the theoretical maximum possible information rate, which was found to be 1,650 bits/s. In essence, the visual system of the fly was found to have information rates within striking distance of the theoretical maximum.

7.7. Maximising Mutual Information

Given that the photoreceptor transfer function $R(f)$ is fixed, the maximum rate at which information can be transmitted from the retinal image to the neuron output depends on the neural filter $G(f)$, which determines the output spectrum. We can deduce the optimal output spectrum (see Section 2.8) under the following assumptions: (a) the average input power has a fixed upper limit, (b) inputs and outputs are Gaussian, and (c) inputs and outputs are related by additive noise, as in Figure 2.1. Assumption (c) can be emulated here by assuming all transfer functions are linear and setting $N_\varepsilon(f)=0$ so that $y=x+\eta$, and therefore Equation 7.15 becomes

$$I(s,y) \quad = \quad \int_f \log \frac{G(f)R(f)S(f) + N_\eta(f)}{N_\eta(f)} \, df \qquad (7.21)$$

$$= \quad \int_f \log V_y(f) \, df - \int_f \log N_\eta(f) \, df \text{ bits}, \qquad (7.22)$$

where

$$V_y(f) \quad = \quad G(f)R(f)S(f) + N_\eta(f) \qquad (7.23)$$

is the neuron output power spectrum, so the output entropy is

$$H(y) \quad = \quad \int_f \log V_y(f) \, df \text{ bits}. \qquad (7.24)$$

Given that the output noise entropy is independent of the system filter $F(f)=G(f)R(f)$, it follows that $I(s,y)\propto H(y)$. Therefore, the system filter $F(f)$ that maximises $H(y)$ also maximises $I(s,y)$. If the noise power is fixed then (given that the signal power is fixed) this implies that the noisy neuron output y power is limited; specifically,

$$\int_f V_y(f)\, df \;\; = \;\; K. \tag{7.25}$$

One more step reveals the underlying nature of the problem. We rewrite Equation 7.24 as a product,

$$H(y) \;\; = \;\; \log \prod_f V_y(f) \text{ bits.} \tag{7.26}$$

Notice that any distribution of $V_y(f)$ values that maximises the product $\prod_f V_y(f)$ also maximises the entropy $H(y)$. Now we can see that the problem consists of finding a value for each of the frequency components $V_y(f)$ so that the product of these components is maximised, subject to the constraint that their sum equals K.

This is a standard problem (originally solved by Shannon[105]), which can be solved by following the same logic as in Section 5.9. Following

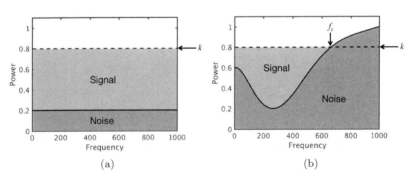

(a)   (b)

Figure 7.14. Schematic representation for maximising information, assuming a limit on output power in Equation 7.25. (a) For a given output noise power spectrum $N_n(f)$ (solid curve), mutual information between the input signal and the output y is maximised if the power $F(f)S(f)$ of the signal at the output (light region) is distributed so that the sum of signal plus noise power $V_y(f)$ has a constant value k across all frequencies (dashed line). (b) If the noise power exceeds k then this defines a cut-off frequency f_c (see text).

that logic, we find that maximising $H(y)$ subject to a constraint on total output variance requires that $V_y(f)=k$, where k is a constant. In other words, to maximise mutual information, the system filter should ensure that the sum of the filtered signal plus neuron output noise power is constant across all frequencies. This means that the power spectrum $V_y(f)$ of the neuron output y is uniform, as shown in Figure 7.14a, where the shaded regions have a total area equal to K. Typically, output noise $N_\eta(f)$ has a uniform power spectrum, as in Figure 7.14a, so the only way to ensure that the spectrum $V_y(f)$ is uniform is to make $F(f)S(f)$ constant; specifically, $F(f)S(f)=k - N_\eta(f)$.

The general strategy outlined above can be applied even if the noise spectrum is not uniform, as in Figure 7.14b. Here, the proportion of noise increases with frequency so that, eventually, $N_\eta(f)=k$, at which point the neuron output y is pure noise. The frequency at which this occurs is called the *cut-off frequency*, f_c. For a given value of k, all values $V_y(f)$ with a frequency greater than f_c are pure noise, so $V_y(f)$ should be set to zero for $f \geq f_c$. Proofs of these results can be found in Cover and Thomas (1991)[30].

7.8. van Hateren's Model

The effect of different luminance conditions on predicted optimal receptive field structures was explored by van Hateren (1992)[120]. Specifically, van Hateren used the model in Figure 7.10 with spectra defined in Equations 7.9–7.13 to explore the neural filter $G(f)$ that maximises mutual information defined in Equation 7.15. He derived two key results, related to high and low signal-to-noise ratios in photoreceptor outputs x. Note that van Hateren assumed the natural luminance spectrum defined in Equation 7.8. He also assumed that photoreceptors impose a Gaussian blur on their inputs (e.g. Figure 7.5), so the photoreceptor filter has a gain defined by

$$\sqrt{R(f)} = e^{-f^2/\sigma}, \qquad (7.27)$$

where $\sigma=0.13$. Crucially, it was assumed that the constraint on power applies to the total neuron output, as in Equation 7.25.

High Photoreceptor Signal-to-Noise Ratio. Under high-luminance conditions, the photoreceptor signal-to-noise ratio is very high, so we can treat the photoreceptor output noise as if it is approximately zero $N_\varepsilon(f) \approx 0$. Under these conditions, van Hateren proved that the optimal neuron filter is defined by

$$G(f)^* \quad = \quad \frac{c_G}{R(f)S(f)}, \tag{7.28}$$

where c_G is a constant. This result was also obtained by Plumbley and Fallside (1991)[93]. Given that $N_\varepsilon(f) = 0$, the neuron output power spectrum is given by Equation 7.23. If $G(f) = G(f)^*$ then the effect of the optimal neural filter $G(f)^*$ on $V_y(f)$ is found by substituting Equation 7.28 in Equation 7.23, so the optimal neuron output power spectrum is

$$V_y(f)^* \quad = \quad c_G + N_\eta(f). \tag{7.29}$$

If the noise is Gaussian then this implies that the optimal neuron output spectrum under high-luminance conditions is uniform. Formally, this is similar to the problem solved by Shannon in Section 7.7, so it is not surprising that the solution is similar.

Because the signal power $S(f)$ and the photoreceptor filter $R(f)$ are both dominated by low frequencies, the optimal neuron filter $G(f)^*$ acts as a high-pass filter. Consequently, the combined effect of a low-pass filter photoreceptor $R(f)$ followed by a high-pass neuron filter $G(f)^*$ is a band-pass filter $R(f)G(f)^*$, which therefore attenuates low and high frequencies in the signal s (see Figure 7.6). The solution for low photoreceptor output noise is shown in Figure 7.15, where the band-pass characteristics of the combined photoreceptor–neuron filter can be seen in Figure 7.15h. Crucially, this is observed under high-luminance conditions in physiological visual systems (Figure 7.12).

Low Photoreceptor Signal-to-Noise Ratio. A more realistic problem involves noise in the outputs of both photoreceptors and neurons. If the photoreceptor output noise is high, $N_\varepsilon(f) >> R(f)S(f)$, then the signal-to-noise ratio in photoreceptor outputs x is low (e.g. under low-luminance conditions). Under these conditions, van

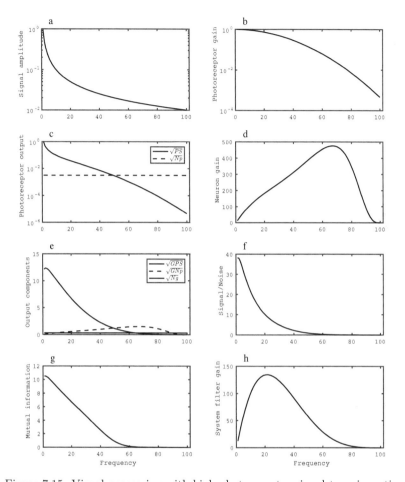

Figure 7.15. Visual processing with high photoreceptor signal-to-noise ratio.
(a) Spectrum of luminance amplitude $S(f)^{1/2}$ in image (Equation 7.8).
(b) Gaussian photoreceptor filter gain $R(f)^{1/2}$ (Equation 7.27).
(c) Signal amplitude at photoreceptor output $(R(f)S(f))^{1/2}$ (solid curve) and photoreceptor noise amplitude $N_\varepsilon(f)^{1/2}$ (dashed line).
(d) Neuron filter gain $G(f)^{1/2}$.
(e) Components of neuron output. Signal amplitude at neuron output $(G(f)R(f)S(f))^{1/2}$ (solid curve). Photoreceptor noise amplitude at neuron output $(G(f)N_\varepsilon(f))^{1/2}$ (dashed curve). Neuron output noise amplitude $N_\eta(f)^{1/2}$ (solid horizontal line, close to abscissa).
(f) Signal-to-noise ratio $(G(f)R(f)S(f)/(G(f)N_\varepsilon(f) + N_\eta(f)))^{1/2}$.
(g) Mutual information (bits) associated with each frequency (Equation 7.15) $I(s(f), y(f)) = \log[1 + S_{op}(f)/N_{op}(f)]$.
(h) The overall system filter gain $F(f)^{1/2} = (G(f)R(f))^{1/2}$ is a band-pass filter, as in Figure 7.12 (modelled as a long-tailed gamma distribution here).

Hateren proved that the optimal neuron filter is defined by

$$G(f)^* \quad \propto \quad (R(f)S(f))^{1/2}. \tag{7.30}$$

Given that the signal power spectrum $S(f)$ is dominated by low frequencies and that the photoreceptor is a low-pass filter $R(f)$, it follows that the optimal neuron filter acts as a (very) low-pass filter. It makes sense to attenuate high image frequencies because, under low-luminance conditions, high frequencies in the image are mostly noise, which yields a non-uniform output spectrum.

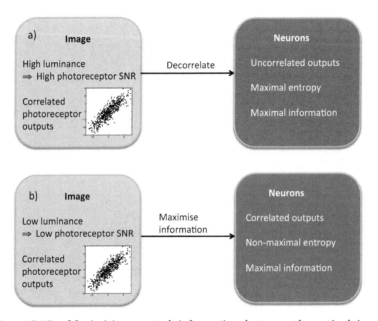

Figure 7.16. Maximising mutual information between the retinal image and outputs of neurons (e.g. ganglion cells). (a) A high-luminance image produces photoreceptor outputs with high signal-to-noise ratios (SNR). In this case, mutual information can be maximised by the proxy strategy of adjusting photoreceptor→neuron connections so that outputs of different neuron are uncorrelated and equivariant, which also maximises neuron output entropy. (b) A low-luminance image produces photoreceptor outputs with low SNRs. In this case, making neuron outputs uncorrelated and equivariant would maximise neuron output entropy but would not maximise mutual information. Maximising mutual information produces correlated neuron outputs and therefore does not maximise the entropy of neuron outputs.

A striking side-effect of such a low-pass filter is that it yields neuron outputs that are more correlated than the corresponding photoreceptor outputs (e.g. Figure 7.5). In this case, neurons effectively use a spatial average of photoreceptor outputs in order to minimise the effects of large amounts of image noise.

The different luminance conditions analysed by van Hateren are summarised in Figure 7.16. Crucially, the filters predicted by information theory[7;120] are similar to those observed in the retina under different lighting conditions, as shown in Figure 7.12 (see Kuffler, 1953[62] and Barlow, Fitzhugh, and Kuffler 1957[16]; but also see Duffy and Hubel, 2007[39] and Vincent and Baddeley, 2003[123]).

7.9. Predictive Coding of Images

Consider an array of filters where each filter is centred on one photoreceptor of the same image such that its receptive field overlaps with the receptive field of several neighbouring filters, as in Figure 7.1. In order to reduce the range (and therefore the power) of ganglion cell output values, we can use the photoreceptor output values within a small image region to form a prediction $\hat{x}_i$ of the photoreceptor output value x_i at the centre of that region. Then, rather than sending the measured photoreceptor output value x_i, we can send the *difference*

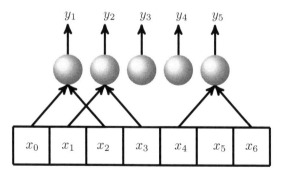

Figure 7.17. The outputs $\mathbf{x}_I = (x_0,...,x_6)$ from a one-dimensional array of photoreceptors are processed by each of five filters with outputs $(y_1,...,y_5)$. Each filter has a receptive field of $m+1=3$ photoreceptors, with $m=2$ weights $\mathbf{w}_1 = (w_{-1}, w_{+1})^T$. For clarity, weights from only three filters are shown.

between x_i and the predicted value $\hat{x}_{it}$,

$$y_{i,t} = (x_{it} - \hat{x}_{it}). \tag{7.31}$$

Notice we have used y to denote the difference, because we will discover that this also approximates the output of a ganglion cell. As in the previous chapter, a useful measure of error, summed over all ganglion cells, is

$$E_s = \sum_{i=1}^{n} y_i^2, \tag{7.32}$$

which is also a measure of the mutual information between the observed photoreceptor value x_i and the predicted photoreceptor value $\hat{x}_i$. The image is n photoreceptor outputs, represented as a row vector

$$x_I = (x_1,...,x_n), \tag{7.33}$$

rather than a two-dimensional array. This does not materially alter the following account, but it does keep the notation uncluttered.

We also assume that each ganglion cell is a linear filter which is connected to a set of m photoreceptors. The m photoreceptors connected to the ith filter define a column vector

$$\mathbf{x}_i = (x_{i-k},...,x_{i-1},x_{i+1},...,x_{i+k})^T, \tag{7.34}$$

where this subset is a substitute for the receptive field of a ganglion cell, as shown in Figure 7.17.

Notice that the photoreceptor output x_i at the centre of the receptive field is missing from $\mathbf{x}_i$, because this is the value to be predicted; so $\mathbf{x}_i$ includes $m=2k$ photoreceptors. In order for a filter to take account of all of the photoreceptors in its receptive field, the filter must also have $m=2k$ weights, represented by the column vector

$$\mathbf{w} = (w_{i-k},...,w_{i-1},w_{i+1},...,w_{i+k})^T. \tag{7.35}$$

The predicted value of the photoreceptor output at the centre of the receptive field is a weighted average of photoreceptor output values in the receptive field,

$$\hat{x}_{i,t} = \sum_{j=-k,j\neq 0}^{k} w_j x_{i-j,t} \tag{7.36}$$

$$= \mathbf{w}^T \mathbf{x}_i, \tag{7.37}$$

where j adopts all values between $-k$ and k except $j=0$. The output of a filter centred on the ith photoreceptor is the difference between this prediction and the neuron output $x_{i,t}$, as defined in Equation 7.31,

$$y_{i,t} = x_{i,t} - \mathbf{w}_s^T \mathbf{x}_{i,t}. \tag{7.38}$$

Least-Squares Estimation. As in the previous chapter, we will find values for the weights which minimise the squared difference or *error* in the predicted value for each photoreceptor output x_i, summed over all n photoreceptors in the image,

$$E_s = \frac{1}{2} \sum_{i=1}^{n} y_i^2 \tag{7.39}$$

$$= \frac{1}{2} \sum_{i=1}^{n} (x_i - \mathbf{w}_s^T \mathbf{x}_i)^2. \tag{7.40}$$

The predicted values of all n photoreceptor outputs in an image are

$$\hat{x} = (\hat{x}_1,...,\hat{x}_n)^T \tag{7.41}$$

$$= \mathbf{w}_s^T (\mathbf{x}_1,...,\mathbf{x}_n). \tag{7.42}$$

The data matrix is defined as

$$X_s = (\mathbf{x}_1,...,\mathbf{x}_n) = \begin{pmatrix} x_{-k,1} & \cdots & x_{1,n} \\ \vdots & & \\ x_{k,1} & \cdots & x_{k,n} \end{pmatrix}, \tag{7.43}$$

where each column is the $m=2k$ photoreceptor output values in the receptive field of one filter (excluding the central photoreceptor output values in row 0), and each row is the n photoreceptor output values in a single image. We can write the errors as a row vector,

$$y \quad = \quad x_I - \mathbf{w}_s{}^T X_s. \tag{7.44}$$

Equation 7.44 has the same form as Equation 6.59, even though the terms here represent spatial variables. We can therefore follow the same logic as applied to Equations 6.59–6.62 to obtain the gradient

$$\nabla E_s \quad = \quad X_s X_s{}^T \mathbf{w}_s - X_s x_I^T. \tag{7.45}$$

At a minimum, $\nabla E_s = 0$, which allows us to conclude that

$$X_s X_s{}^T \mathbf{w}_s \quad = \quad X_s x_I^T, \tag{7.46}$$

and therefore

$$\mathbf{w}_s \quad = \quad (X_s X_s{}^T)^{-1} X_s x_I^T. \tag{7.47}$$

As noted previously, Equation 7.47 provides a solution, but it does not provide much insight. For this, we will take a more circuitous route to the same solution as above.

First, note that in Equation 7.46 we can invoke the law of large numbers, so that if $n \gg m$ then

$$\mathbb{C}_s \quad = \quad \mathrm{E}[X_s X_s{}^T], \tag{7.48}$$

where $\mathbb{C}_s$ is an $m \times m$ covariance matrix

$$\mathbb{C}_s \quad = \quad \begin{pmatrix} R_{-k,-k}, & \cdots, & R_{-k,k} \\ & \vdots & \\ R_{k,-k}, & \cdots, & R_{k,k} \end{pmatrix},$$

where the diagonal elements of R are photoreceptor variances and the off-diagonal elements are covariances between photoreceptors,

$$R_{ii} = \text{var}(i) \tag{7.49}$$

$$R_{ij} = \text{cov}(i,j). \tag{7.50}$$

Second, consider the final term in Equation 7.46, which is $X_s x_I$. Each row in X_s is an image with n elements, where the first photoreceptor output in the ith row x_i of X_s has a value equal to the $(i - k)$th photoreceptor output in the image x_I. So the expected value of the inner product of the ith row of X_s with x_I is x_I multiplied by itself, but shifted by i photoreceptors,

$$\mathbb{R}_i = \text{E}[x_i\, x_I^T] \tag{7.51}$$

$$= \text{E}[x_{I-i}\, x_I^T]. \tag{7.52}$$

As above, the mean value of this inner product yields the covariance between photoreceptors separated by a distance of i photoreceptors. When considered over all possible distances, this defines the spatial autocorrelation function $\mathbb{R}_i$ of the image, such that $\mathbb{R}_i = \text{cov}(0,i)$. We can now rewrite Equation 7.46 in terms of the covariance matrix $\mathbb{C}_s$ and the autocorrelation function

$$\mathbb{R} = \mathbb{C}_s \mathbf{w}_s. \tag{7.53}$$

When rearranged as $\mathbb{C}_s \mathbf{w}_s = \mathbb{R}$, it is apparent that Equation 7.53 represents $m = 2k$ simultaneous equations with $2k$ unknowns ($\mathbf{w}_s$),

$$
\begin{aligned}
R_{-k,-k} w_{-k} + & \quad \ldots, \quad + R_{-k,k} w_k &= R_{-k} \\
\vdots & \qquad\qquad\quad \vdots \qquad &= \vdots \\
R_{k,-k} w_{-k} + & \quad \ldots \quad + R_{k,k} w_k &= R_k.
\end{aligned}
\tag{7.54}
$$

Notice that the autocorrelation function R_τ at a spatial offset of τ photoreceptors is estimated as the (same) linear combination of autocorrelation values at m different spatial offsets (in the τth row on the left-hand side). The solution to this set of simultaneous equations is a set of weights $\mathbf{w}_s$, which is the least-squares estimate of the optimal prediction filter weights $\mathbf{w}_s^*$. A spatial version of the proof in Chapter 6 guarantees that prediction errors are uncorrelated.

7.10. Evidence for Predictive Coding

Predictive coding has been tested using detailed data from the fly (see Section 6.8). Under high-luminance conditions (and based on measured photoreceptor outputs, which provide some normalisation), the least-squares estimate of filter weights was found to be a good match to the typical Mexican hat receptive field structure of the large monopolar cells (LMC) in the fly, as shown in Figure 7.18. Using extensive tests, Srinivasan et al. (1982)[112] found that predictive coding also provides good matches under widely varying lighting conditions. Similar results based on predictive coding have been reported in a model of the vertebrate retina[52].

The receptive fields obtained with predictive coding (Figure 7.18) and information maximisation (Figure 7.12) are similar. However, in principle, they can only be identical under high-luminance conditions (i.e. if photoreceptor noise is effectively zero). This is because predictive coding necessarily produces uncorrelated outputs y, which (assuming these are Gaussian and equivariant) also have maximum entropy. In contrast, maximising mutual information produces uncorrelated outputs only under high-luminance conditions (see Figure 7.16).

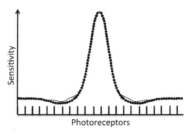

Figure 7.18. Predictive coding. Mexican hat profile typical of visual neurons. Solid curve (mostly hidden by dotted curve): measured response of fly large monopolar cell response, showing inhibitory region. Dotted curve: response based on predictive coding of the natural statistics of images (Figure 7.11a). Modified from Srinivasan et al. (1982)[112].

The general principle of predictive coding has been extended by Rao and Ballard (1999)[95] by incorporating long-range feedback connections from the primary visual cortex into the model. On a grander scale, predictive coding is a key element in Friston's influential free-energy theory of brain function[20;103].

7.11. Is Receptive Field Spacing Optimal?

Ganglion cells do not exist in isolation, but as part of a spatial array. We now address this question: which combination of receptive field size and spacing transmits as much information as possible about the image? The following is a summary of Borghuis et al. (2008)[21] and Balasubramanian and Sterling (2009)[13] (also see Doi et al., 2012[38]).

For a fixed spacing, increasing the receptive field size brings good news and bad news. The good news is that a larger receptive field means that the ganglion cell input is a weighted average of a large number of photoreceptors, which reduces the effects of photoreceptor noise. Of course, as receptive field size increases (or, equivalently, as spacing decreases), the overlap between receptive fields increases; which brings us to the bad news. If ganglion cells have overlapping receptive fields then they share some photoreceptors, which increases the correlation between ganglion cell outputs. Indeed, even if receptive fields share no photoreceptors, the spatial correlations within each

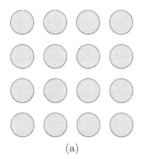
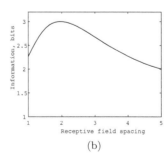

(a) (b)

Figure 7.19. (a) If the spacing between receptive fields is large then ganglion cell outputs are independent, but some parts of the image are not covered by any receptive field. (b) How spacing between receptive fields affects the collective information conveyed by an array of model (DoG) ganglion cells. Schematic graph of results obtained by Borghuis et al. (2008)[21].

image means that nearby ganglion cells have correlated inputs. So larger receptive fields increase the signal-to-noise ratio of individual ganglion cells, but the resultant correlations between their inputs can reduce the information in the collective outputs of ganglion cells. The result is a trade-off between receptive field size and spacing.

Borghuis et al. (2008)[21] used numerical simulations to find the ratio of receptive field size to receptive field spacing which yields the maximum mutual information conveyed by an array of ganglion cells. They defined receptive field size as $\sigma = \sqrt{v_E}$, which is the standard deviation of the excitatory centre of a DoG filter (Equation 7.7).

The receptive field spacing which maximises information for natural images was found to be about 2σ, as shown in Figure 7.19b, and this result held true. Crucially, this result is similar to values observed in the retina across a variety of different ganglion cell types. If the number of ganglion cells is fixed then a spacing of 2σ not only maximises information, it also maximises information per ganglion cell; it is therefore both coding efficient and metabolically efficient. Finally, there is evidence that the distribution[124] and structure[123] of receptive fields is metabolically efficient.

7.12. Summary

In attempting to find a satisfactory model of visual processing, we could have measured the inputs and outputs of ganglion cells and then estimated the parameter values (weights) of a spatial filter which mimicked those inputs and outputs. But we already know (from Chapter 6) that such a strategy works very well in the temporal domain. Instead, we have chosen to use efficiency as a guiding principle in assessing the structure receptive fields, and we have found that the ganglion cell receptive field structures predicted by information theory and (under certain circumstances) predictive coding are remarkably similar to those observed in the retina. A striking feature of both predictive coding and information-theoretic models is that they are not designed to mimic physiological receptive fields; their only objective is to maximise information throughput. The implications of this observation are as compelling as they are self-evident.

Chapter 8

Encoding Visual Contrast

... in neural design, what is most efficient in theory is not always most efficient in practice because neural implementation stands in the way.
Sterling and Laughlin, 2015.

8.1. Introduction

In this chapter, we will see how certain neurons in the fly's visual system have a transfer (input → output) function which is 'tuned' to the visual world in which the fly lives. This tuning of the transfer function allows the fly's visual system to access as much information as possible, so we refer to it as *maximum entropy encoding* here. The combination of predictive coding followed by maximum entropy encoding provides an overall strategy[66;113] summarised in Figure 8.2. But first, we will review the anatomy of fly visual systems.

8.2. The Compound Eye

Insects have *compound eyes* (Figure 8.1), which consist of a large number of facets or *ommatidia*, where each ommatidium has its own lens. Each ommatidium is basically a tube with a lens at the top, which focuses light on to the upper surface of a long *rhabdom*. The rhabdom comprises eight light-sensitive neurons called *rhabdomeres*, labelled as R1–R8, where each rhabdomere acts as a light guide. Two rhabdomeres (R7 and R8) lie one on top of the other, so we will treat them as if they are a single rhabdomere.

The overall structure of the image recorded by the array of ommatidia is preserved through the first few layers of the visual system. Thus, the ommatidia project to the *lamina*, and each ommatidium projects to one or more *lamina cartridge*, each of which contains *large monopolar cells* (LMC). The array of lamina cartridges projects (one-to-one) to a corresponding array of *medulla cartridges*. To a first approximation, we can treat each cartridge of the lamina and medulla as the equivalent of a 'neural pixel' in the image received by the insect's brain.

Even though all compound eyes look superficially similar, there are three basic designs: *apposition, optical superposition*, and *neural superposition* (see Land and Nilsson, 2002[63]). In terms of efficiency, the biggest difference is between apposition and neural superposition eyes, so we will concentrate on those here.

Apposition Eyes.   Apposition eyes are relatively simple, and are possessed by most diurnal insects and crustaceans (e.g. bees, grasshoppers, crabs), the 'living fossil' horseshoe crab (*Limulus*) and the actual fossil trilobites (from 520 million years ago)[63].   In an apposition eye, all of the rhabdomeres in each ommatidium comprise a single fused structure within a narrow rhabdom, and its outputs project to one lamina cartridge.

For example, each rhabdom in a worker bee occupies a small, roughly circular area in the middle of the ommatidium's field of view; so light within the ommatidium that strikes the area surrounding the rhabdom

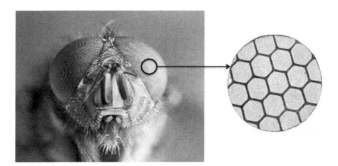

Figure 8.1. Compound eyes of *Calliphora vomitoria*, with magnified region showing hexagonal arrangement some of the 6,000 ommatidia in each eye. Photograph by JJ Harrison, Creative Commons Attribution 3.0 License.

represents wasted information. Each rhabdom is smaller than the ommatidium to ensure that the field of view of rhabdoms in adjacent ommatidia do not overlap, so rhabdoms in adjacent ommatidia have abutting or *apposing* fields of view.

Neural Superposition Eyes. Fast-flying diurnal insects like the housefly (*Musca domestica*), the fruitfly (*Drosophila melanogaster*), and the bluebottle fly (*Calliphora vomitoria*) use an ingenious design, neural superposition, which Land and Nilsson (2002)[63] aptly describe as a precise form of 'neural knitting' (Figure 8.3). This neural knitting maximises information transmission through metabolically expensive structures like the eye and lamina; a blowfly resting in sunlight uses 10% of its energy to support its photoreceptors and LMCs[114].

The rhabdomeres within each ommatidium of a neural superposition eye are not fused but are arranged approximately geometrically around a central rhabdomere, so that most of the ommatidial visual field is captured by the seven rhabdomeres. The six outer rhabdomeres (R1–R6) project to different LMCs within the lamina, whereas the central rhabdomere axons (R7/8) pass through the lamina (without making synaptic connections) and project to the medulla. The arrangement of

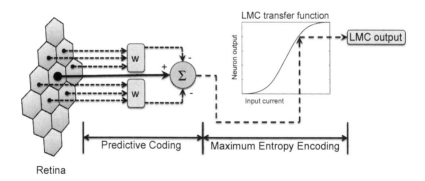

Figure 8.2. Schematic overview of two stages of encoding: predictive coding and maximum entropy encoding. Each hexagon represents one retinal facet or ommatidium. In principle, spatial predictive coding could be obtained by mutual inhibition between retinal ommatidia and between rhabdomeres within adjacent ommatidia[66]. Temporal predictive coding is obtained via the LMC impulse response function (Section 6.8). The symbol **w** represents a weighted sum of rhabdomere outputs; these weights collectively implement a receptive field akin to ganglion cell receptive fields (Chapter 7).

ommatidia in the neural superposition eye, and of rhabdomeres within each ommatidium, ensures that light rays from a single point in a scene excite different rhabdomeres in adjacent ommatidia. Specifically, the angle (1.5 degrees) *between adjacent ommatidia* is the same as the angle between adjacent rhabdomeres *within each ommatidium*. Consequently, seven rhabdomeres in a cluster of seven neighbouring ommatidia see the *same* part of the scene in front of the fly.

For example, the 'central' rhabdomere R7 in one ommatidium receives light from the same point in the scene as rhabdomere R1 in an adjacent ommatidium, R2 in the next ommatidium, and so on. However, only the six outer rhabdomeres project to (different) LMC neurons. Thus, each LMC ('neural pixel') effectively collates information from six rhabdomeres within six different ommatidia, where all six rhabdomeres are 'looking at' the same point in the scene (Figure 8.3). Each rhabdomere is connected to each LMC via approximately 220 synapses, so that each LMC receives information regarding a single scene point via $1320(=6 \times 220)$ synapses[68].

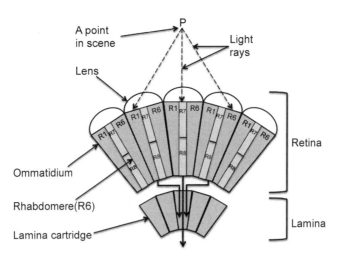

Figure 8.3.   Neural superposition.   Schematic cross-section of retina showing five ommatidia. Each ommatidium contains eight light-sensitive *rhabdomeres*, (only R1, R6, R7, and R8 are shown). Eight rhabdomeres in seven different ommatidia (arranged in a hexagon) 'look at' the same scene point P, and their outputs converge on one cartridge of the medulla (which lies below the lamina).

Given that each LMC receives the output of six rhabdomeres, the signal-to-noise ratio of each LMC should be six times larger than that of each rhabdomere, as confirmed in Laughlin, Howard, and Blakeslee (1987)[68], but not in van Hateren (1992)[120].

For completeness, in *Calliphora*, each rhabdomere can provide up to $R_{info} \approx 1,000$ bits/s of mutual information, whereas each LMC can provide up to $R_{info} \approx 1,650$ bits/s[34]. Recent studies by Juusola[57;58] report information rates even higher than these.

8.3. Not Wasting Capacity

If you were a neuron, why would you care about the information or the entropy of your output values? Because, in order to transmit as much information as possible to your output about your inputs, you need to ensure that the distribution of your output values is a maximum entropy distribution.

However, the precise form of a maximum entropy distribution of outputs depends on the constraints that apply to those outputs (as described in Chapter 2). In short, if outputs are constrained by having limited energy, but with an unlimited range, then the maximum entropy distribution is Gaussian. In contrast, if outputs are constrained by having definite bounds on their range then the maximum entropy distribution is uniform. However, if we compare a uniform distribution with other distributions having the same range (e.g. a triangular distribution) then they can have higher efficiencies, so the uniform distribution is not the most metabolically efficient. Thus, given a fixed energy budget, the Gaussian distribution maximises both coding efficiency and metabolic efficiency, whereas the uniform distribution maximises coding efficiency but not metabolic efficiency.

It matters whether the dominant constraint for neurons is energy or output range because it defines which distribution maximises their information throughput. In practice, it is difficult to know which constraint is dominant, so we will consider both, but we will explore the consequences of a fixed range in detail, as described in Laughlin's classic 1981 paper[64].

8.4. Measuring the Eye's Response

In order to record the effect of different contrasts on the LMC, Laughlin's fly was placed in front of a screen which contained a light emitting diode (LED), as shown in Figure 8.4. Over many trials, the contrast between the LED and the screen was varied by increasing or decreasing the LED luminance.

At the start of each trial, the luminance L of the LED was set to be the same as the screen luminance $\overline{L}$. The LED luminance was then changed to a new luminance L for 100 ms. The contrast induced by a change in LED luminance from its initial value of $\overline{L}$ to I is $s=\Delta L/\overline{L}$, where $\Delta L=L-\overline{L}$. This defines contrast as a temporal change in LED luminance, where this change is expressed as a proportion of the initial LED luminance. So, in this experiment, the contrast s is both the contrast between the LED and its background and the contrast between the initial and final luminance of the LED. The response of the LMC to different contrasts is shown in Figure 8.5.

In fact, the transfer function of photoreceptors is approximately logarithmic, which makes their outputs proportional to contrast, not luminance (brightness)[114]. This is desirable because the range of luminances under natural conditions far outstrips the *dynamic range* of photoreceptor outputs. The output of a typical photoreceptor can change by a factor of about 100, but (for example) the difference

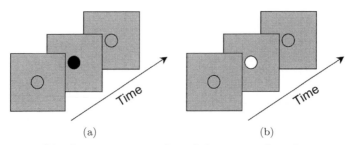

(a)   (b)

Figure 8.4. Stimulus sequences used to elicit response from *large monopolar cells* (LMC) in the fly's brain. The central disc represents an LED light, which is initially at the same luminance as the background. The LED luminance is changed for 100 ms and then reverts to its initial luminance.
(a) Contrast changes from zero to negative (LED made dimmer) to zero.
(b) Contrast changes from zero to positive (LED made brighter) to zero.

between sunlight and moonlight represents a luminance change factor of about 100,000. In order to accommodate such a large range of luminance, the photoreceptors (of flies and vertebrates) adapt, using a type of *automatic gain control*. Without such adaptation, photoreceptors outputs would be either constantly high (e.g. in bright sunlight) or constantly low (i.e. in dim light)[114]. An additional benefit is that power requirements are reduced, for the same reasons that predictive coding reduces power (see Sections 6.6 and 7.9).

What the Fly's Eye Sees. Laughlin used a special camera to film the fly's world, from the fly's perspective. He did this by using coloured filters and image blurring operators to ensure that his camera could see only what a fly would see (in terms of wavelength and spatial frequency, respectively). As a result, Laughlin had a record of the fly's experience of the world, expressed in terms of contrast s.

At this point, Laughlin had two sets of data: (1) the LMC responses to different contrasts, shown in Figure 8.5, and (2) a record of the contrasts experienced by the fly, which define a skewed histogram, similar to the distribution in Figure 8.6a. As will be explained in this chapter, if the fly's eye transmits information in accord with the efficient coding hypothesis then the predicted LMC transfer function

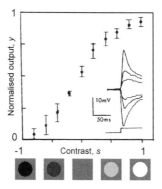

Figure 8.5. How image contrast affects the output of a LMC neuron. Inset shows transient voltage change following a single change in contrast (LMCs hyperpolarise to increments and depolarise to decrements in contrast). A response was defined to be the peak of this transient change. Each point plotted in Figure 8.5 is an average response, where this average is taken over many trials and over six LMCs. Vertical bars show total scatter. Modified from Laughlin (1981)[64], Creative Commons Attribution 3.0 License.

is obtained by adding up the area under the contrast distribution and plotting it in the form of a cumulative total, as in Figures 8.6c and 8.7. Let's call this cumulative total the *optimal transfer function* (because, as we shall see, that's what it is).

However, although this theoretical prediction of LMC responses varies between zero and one, there is no reason why LMC responses should do so. Laughlin therefore normalised the LMC responses so that they varied between zero and one, so that for a given measured LMC voltage v obtained in response to a contrast change $s = \Delta I / \overline{I}$, the normalised response y was defined as $y = (v - v_{min})/(v_{max} - v_{min})$, where v_{min} and v_{max} are responses to the largest negative and positive contrast, respectively.

8.5. Maximum Entropy Encoding

In essence, the question we seek to answer is this: given that the probability distribution of s is fixed by the environment, what form should the transfer function g take to ensure that the (noiseless) channel outputs y convey as much information as possible about the channel outputs $y = g(s)$? In other words, how should g be adjusted to maximise the mutual information between s and y?

In order to answer this question we need to know how the entropies of s and y are related, given that $y = g(s) + \eta$. As previously, we assume zero noise, so that $y = g(s)$: an assumption which seems to be justified physiologically [114]. The mutual information between input (contrast) and output is

$$I(s,y) \quad = \quad H(g(s)) - H(\eta) \text{ bits,} \qquad (8.1)$$

and if $\text{var}(\eta) \approx 0$ then $H(\eta) \approx 0$, so

$$I(s,y) \quad \approx \quad H(g(s)) \text{ bits.} \qquad (8.2)$$

Thus, we can maximise the mutual information by finding a transfer function g that maximises the entropy of the LMC output y.

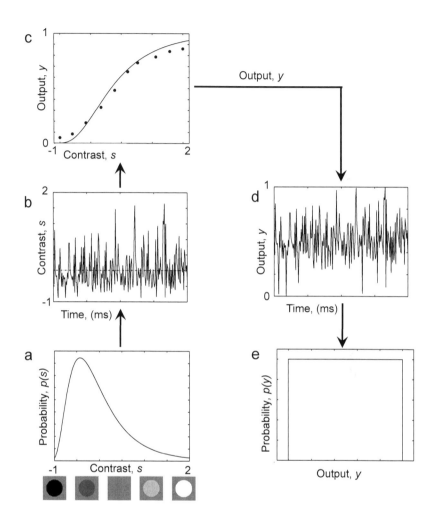

Figure 8.6. Schematic summary of Laughlin's experiment.
(a) Probability density function $p_s(s)$ of contrasts s in the fly's environment.
(b) Sampled values of s from (a) obtained over time as the fly moves around.
(c) Transforming s values to (normalised) output values y using the cumulative distribution function (cdf) of $p_s(s)$, which is the optimal encoding function g^* (smooth curve) and which predicts the outputs $y=g(s)$ of LMC neurons (dots).
(d) How normalised LMC outputs y change over time.
(e) Uniform probability density function $p_y(y)$ of LMC outputs.

Maximising Mutual Information by Maximising Entropy.
Given that $I(s,y)$ varies as a function of g, when $I(s,y)$ is as large as possible, the slope of $I(s,y)$ with respect to g must be zero. It follows that if we want to find that particular g which maximises $I(s,y)$ then we need to find a form for g which makes the derivative (slope) of $I(s,y)$ with respect to g equal to zero,

$$\frac{\partial I(s,y)}{\partial g(s)} = 0. \tag{8.3}$$

Given our zero-noise assumption, Equation 8.2 implies that

$$\frac{\partial I(s,y)}{\partial g(s)} = \frac{dH(y)}{dg(s)}. \tag{8.4}$$

For a channel with bounded output values (e.g. 0 to 1), the distribution $p(y)$ with maximum entropy is the uniform distribution (see Section 2.4). Therefore, to maximise the mutual information, we need a form for the function g that makes the distribution $p(y)$ uniform.

In practice, the distribution of contrasts experienced by a fly has the skewed shape shown in Figure 8.6a. This skewed shape resembles a lognormal distribution in which the probability (density) of each contrast s is

$$p_s(s) = \frac{1}{s\sigma\sqrt{2\pi}}\exp\left(-\frac{(\mu - \ln s)^2}{2\sigma^2}\right), \tag{8.5}$$

where μ is the mean and σ is the standard deviation. Next, we will explore how changing the transfer function g affects the entropy of y.

Entropy of a Function. If $y = g(s)$ then every value of s between a specific value s_1 and $s_1 + \Delta s$ gets mapped to a corresponding value between $y_1 = g(s_1)$ and $y_1 + \Delta y = g(s_1 + \Delta s)$ (see Figure 8.7). For a small interval Δs around s_1,

$$\text{Prob}(s_1 < s \leq [s_1 + \Delta s]) \approx p(s)\Delta s, \tag{8.6}$$

and for a small interval Δy around a corresponding value $y_1 = g(s_1)$,

$$\text{Prob}(y_1 < y \leq [y_1 + \Delta y]) \approx p(y)\Delta y, \tag{8.7}$$

where $p_s(s)\Delta s \approx p_y(y)\Delta y$. If $y=g(s)$ is monotonic then

$$p_y(y) \quad \approx \quad \frac{p_s(s)}{\Delta y/\Delta s}. \qquad (8.8)$$

In the limit $\Delta y \to 0$,

$$p(y) \quad = \quad \frac{p_s(s)}{dy/ds}. \qquad (8.9)$$

If we define the probability density function as $f(s)=dy/ds$ then

$$p_y(y) \quad = \quad \frac{p_s(s)}{f(s)}. \qquad (8.10)$$

The entropy of y is

$$H(y) \quad = \quad \int_{-\infty}^{\infty} p_y(y) \log \frac{1}{p_y(y)} \, dy \text{ bits.} \qquad (8.11)$$

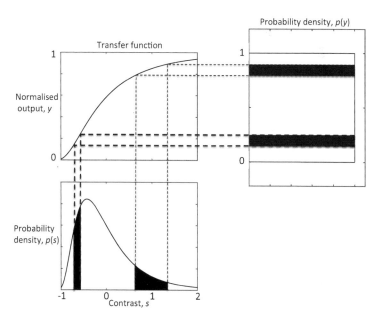

Figure 8.7. Contrasts s in the environment have a distribution $p(s)$ (bottom). Each contrast gets mapped to an output y by a transfer function (top left). If this transfer function is the cumulative distribution function of $p(s)$ then unequal increments of contrast map to equal increments of response (top right). All shaded regions have the same area (probability).

Crucially, because y has fixed bounds, $H(y)$ is maximal only if $p_y(y)$ is uniform (see Chapter 2). Substituting Equation 8.10 into 8.11,

$$H(y) \quad = \quad \int_y \frac{p_s(s)}{f(s)} \left(\log \frac{f(s)}{p_s(s)} \right) dy. \qquad (8.12)$$

Substituting $dy = f(s)ds$ yields

$$H(y) \quad = \quad \int_s p_s(s) \, \log \frac{f(s)}{p_s(s)} \, ds. \qquad (8.13)$$

Given that $H(y)$ is maximised only if $p(y)$ is uniform and that $p(y) = f(s)/p_s(s)$, it follows that the ratio $f(s)/p_s(s)$ should be the same for all values of s.

Which Transfer Function Maximises Entropy? Given that $p_s(s)$ and $f(s)$ are probability density functions (i.e. with areas that sum to one), the ratio $f(s)/p_s(s)$ can be constant only if $p_s(s) = f(s)$. What does this equality imply about the transfer function?

Well, the derivative of the transfer function is $f(s) = dg(s)/ds$, so, by definition, the transfer function is given by the integral of $f(s)$,

$$g(s) \quad = \quad \int_{t=-\infty}^{s} f(t) \, dt, \qquad (8.14)$$

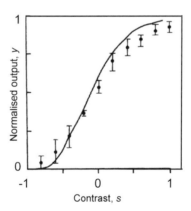

Figure 8.8. The main result from Laughlin's experiment. How image contrast, affects neuronal output, as indicated by small black discs. The solid curve is a theoretical prediction based on the frequency of contrasts in the fly's environment (Equation 8.15). Modified from Laughlin (1981)[64], Creative Commons Attribution 3.0 License.

where $g(s)$ is the *cumulative distribution function* of $f(s)$. Similarly, the cdf of the probability distribution $p_s(s)$ is

$$g^*(s) \quad = \quad \int_{t=-\infty}^{s} p_s(t) \, dt, \tag{8.15}$$

where $g(s)^*$ is the optimal transfer function. Therefore, if the transfer function $g(s)$ is adjusted such that its derivative $dg(s)/ds$ has the same magnitude as $p_s(s)$ then $g(s)=g^*(s)$. In summary, if we want to ensure that each output value y carries as much information as possible then we must ensure that the transfer function $g(s)$ is the same as the optimal transfer function, which is the cdf $g^*(s)$ of $p_s(s)$.

8.6. Evidence for Maximum Entropy Encoding

When Laughlin plotted the optimal transfer function (i.e. the cumulative distribution function of contrasts) of the camera data he had collected and the normalised LMC responses on the same axes, he obtained Figure 8.8. The fit between the two data sets reported in Laughlin (1981)[64] is not perfect, but later work by Laughlin et al.[68;114] revealed a remarkable similarity between the LMC transfer function and the cdf of contrasts. This later work also reported that the transfer function becomes more shallow as luminance is reduced and is a straight line at very low luminances. Reducing luminance increases noise in photoreceptor outputs, which has a flat distribution[68]. Because the cdf of a flat distribution is a straight line, this is the only LMC transfer function capable of producing a uniform output distribution.

More recent research has shown that the fly's eye adapts rapidly to overall changes in light levels to maximise information transmission[25;41]. This general approach has been applied to other species[65] and on other sense modalities, such as speech perception[108], audition in the cricket[97], and olfaction in the moth[61] and the locust[43].

A Caveat. The LMC response (voltage) at each instant is a function of the temporal sequence of stimulus values from the recent past. Using a temporal stimulus sequence of stimulus values, van Hateren (1997)[122] reported that the distribution of LMC response voltages is approximately Gaussian; unlike the uniform distribution of LMC *peak* voltages in Figure 8.6e, which are idealised responses to the isolated contrasts shown in Figure 8.4.

Taken together, the results of Laughlin and van Hateren present a conundrum. The peak responses to isolated contrasts have a uniform distribution, which is coding efficient, but not metabolically efficient (see Section 8.3), whereas the responses to temporal sequences have a Gaussian distribution, which is both coding efficient and metabolically efficient. Consequently, Laughlin's elegant analysis of LMC peak responses and their distribution may provide only a rough guide to the question of whether LMC responses are optimally (uniformly) distributed under natural conditions.

8.7. Summary

Just as the temporal and spatial predictive coding models provided precise fits to the temporal and spatial results observed physiologically, so Laughlin's model yields a remarkably precise fit to the transfer function of LMCs. And this model is impressive for the same reason that those predictive coding models are: there are *no free parameters*. This indicates that LMCs encode isolated contrasts to maximise coding efficiency (but not metabolic efficiency). Additionally, the finding that the distribution of LMC outputs is Gaussian in response to temporal sequences[122] suggests that LMCs encode sequences to maximise both coding efficiency and metabolic efficiency.

Chapter 9

The Neural Rubicon

It is no good poking around in the brain without some idea of what one is looking for. That would be like trying to find a needle in a haystack without having any idea what needles look like. The theorist is the man who might reasonably be asked for his opinion about the appearance of needles.

HC Longuet-Higgins, 1969.

9.1. Introduction

Scientists develop working models of how particular components (e.g. cells, genes) perform a given task. Initially, these models take the form of mechanisms, which explain *how* the biological system under consideration works. This is a necessary part of the scientific process. But, eventually, we want to know the answer to a deeper question: not how, but *why?*

9.2. The Darwinian Cost of Efficiency

Just as a bird cannot fly without obeying the laws of physics, so a brain cannot function without obeying the laws of information. And, just as the shape of a bird's wing is ultimately determined by the laws of physics, so the structure of a neuron is ultimately determined by the laws of information (as stated in Chapter 1). These laws dictate that the cost of information rises steeply with the rate at which information is transmitted, which suggests that neurons should transmit information at the lowest energy cost. However, the high metabolic cost of information is worthwhile if it increases Darwinian fitness; so we cannot disregard the possibility that high information rates obtained at a high metabolic cost should be observed physiologically. But we should also expect the default scenario to minimise metabolic cost.

It could be argued that evolution does not select individuals according to their metabolic efficiency or coding efficiency, but according to their *fitness efficiency*; that is, the amount of Darwinian fitness gained per Joule of expended energy. As mentioned in Chapter 1, it is difficult to formalise the notion of fitness, so we have chosen a plausible proxy for fitness here: metabolic efficiency.

However, we should always bear in mind that any putative computational principle intended to embody fitness is implemented by neurons, which have multiple constraints on their physical structure. Such considerations are aptly summarised by the quote from Sterling and Laughlin (2015)[114] that opens Chapter 8, repeated here:

> ...*in neural design, what is most efficient in theory is not always most efficient in practice because neural implementation stands in the way.*

So, even though we seek general principles that can act as a dominant driver for neural design, we might expect that the physical implementation of any given principle will usually yield a compromise between what is desirable and what is possible: between an idealised platonic theory and the harsh reality of biological implementation.

Accordingly, on a graph with metabolic efficiency on one axis and coding efficiency (information throughput) on the other, we expect neural components with different requirements to be located over a range of values along both axes. However, what we observe physiologically is subtly, but fundamentally, different from this (see Figure 9.1). The metabolic efficiency of the mean firing rate (and other parameters) is not just large, it is about as large as is theoretically possible. It is as though neurons demand maximal metabolic efficiency, and they are not prepared to trade an iota of this metabolic efficiency simply to increase coding efficiency. Of course, such a trade is irrelevant for parameters which possess both metabolic and coding efficiency (e.g. iid Gaussian variables).

In summary, the evidence presented in previous chapters suggests that the following physiological parameters have been optimised by natural selection to ensure that (subject to various physical constraints) information is transmitted at the lowest metabolic cost (Figure 9.1):

1. average firing rate (Chapter 4)
2. distribution of firing rates (Chapter 4)
3. most common axon diameter in the optic nerve (Chapter 4)
4. distribution of axon diameters in axon bundles (Chapter 4)
5. conductance of retinal ganglion cell synapses (Chapter 4)
6. recombination of red, green, and blue cone outputs into retinal ganglion cell inputs (Chapter 5)
7. temporal receptive field structures, which determine responses to time-varying inputs (Chapter 6)
8. spatial receptive field structures, which determine responses to spatial patterns (Chapter 7)
9. size and spacing of ganglion cell receptive fields (Chapter 7).

In essence, fundamental aspects of neural computation are consistent with the hypothesis that neurons maximise metabolic efficiency. Indeed, the evidence is sufficiently compelling that it may be more appropriate to call this the *efficient metabolic principle*.

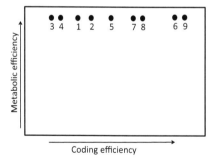

Figure 9.1. Schematic summary of results listed above, where each numbered dot corresponds to one result. The position of each dot along the ordinate is reasonably accurate, but the position along the abscissa is a rough guess. The main point is that all dots represent extremely high metabolic efficiencies.

9.3. Crossing the Neural Rubicon

Before we have understood a biological function, like colour perception, we first ask how it could possibly be implemented by a mechanism within the eye or brain. But after we have acquired a rigorous understanding of the physiological mechanisms which implement that function, we can ask a deeper, more interesting question: why is the function implemented in that particular way? For example, why do we see colour aftereffects, and why do aftereffects occur in the pairs red/green and blue/yellow?

Answering such *why* questions can then lead to an understanding of the nature of the limits on energy, time, and information, which constrain Nature's design of the physiological mechanisms under consideration. Indeed, once we have a precise account of these constraints, we soon come to appreciate that what began as a question regarding *how* a particular function is implemented as a physiological mechanism leads naturally to questions about *why* the mechanism is implemented as it is.

In the context of neural computation, the evidence collated from a wide variety of research papers suggests that a plausible candidate regarding why physiological mechanisms work in the particular way they do is because they maximise the amount of information gained for each Joule of energy expended (i.e. to maximise metabolic efficiency). In the process of testing this hypothesis, we have found that most functions (like colour opponency) which were once perceived as mysterious are actually implemented in ways that are inevitable, and even obvious, when considered 'in the light of evolution': specifically, in the context of neural information theory.

Now that we have crossed that Rubicon which treats questions regarding the *why* of neural computation as seriously as questions regarding the *how*, what have we gained? We have gained information regarding the appearance of needles. And, if we are sufficiently diligent, a needle.

Further Reading

Bialek, W (2012)[18]. *Biophysics*. A comprehensive and rigorous account of the physics which underpins biological processes, including neuroscience and morphogenesis. Bialek adopts the information-theoretic approach which was so successfully applied in his previous book, *Spikes*[98]. The writing style is fairly informal, but this book assumes a high level of mathematical competence. Highly recommended.

Dayan, P and Abbott, LF (2001)[33]. *Theoretical Neuroscience*. This classic text is a comprehensive and rigorous account of computational neuroscience, which demands a high level of mathematical competence.

Eliasmith, C and Anderson, CH (2004)[40]. *Neural Engineering*. Technical account which stresses the importance of linearisation using opponent processing, and nonlinear encoding in the presence of linear decoding.

Gerstner, W and Kistler, WM (2002)[47]. *Spiking Neuron Models: Single Neurons, Populations, Plasticity*. Excellent text on models of the detailed dynamics of neurons.

Land, MF and Nilsson, DE (2002)[63]. *Animal Eyes*. New York: Oxford University Press. A landmark book by two of the most authoritative exponents of the intricacies of eye design.

Marr, D (1982, republished 2010)[77]. *Vision: A Computational Investigation into the Human Representation and Processing of Visual Information*. This classic book inspired a generation of vision scientists to explore the computational approach, succinctly summarised in this famous quotation: 'Trying to understand perception by studying only neurons is like trying to understand bird flight by studying only feathers: It just cannot be done'.

Reza, FM (1961)[96]. *An Introduction to Information Theory*. Comprehensive and mathematically rigorous, with a reasonably geometric approach.

Rieke, F, Warland, D, de Ruyter van Steveninck, RR, and Bialek, W (1997)[98]. *Spikes: Exploring the Neural Code*. The first modern text to formulate questions about the functions of single neurons in terms of information theory. Superbly written in a tutorial style, well argued, and fearless in its pursuit of solid answers to hard questions. Research papers by these authors are highly recommended for their clarity.

Sterling, P and Laughlin, S (2015)[114]. *Principles of Neural Design*. Comprehensive and detailed account of how information theory constrains the design of neural systems. Sterling and Laughlin interpret physiological findings from a wide range of organisms in terms of a single unifying framework: Shannon's mathematical theory of information. A remarkable book, highly recommended.

Zhaoping, L (2014)[126]. *Understanding Vision: Theory, Models, and Data*. Contemporary account of vision based mainly on the efficient coding hypothesis. Even though this book is technically demanding, the introductory chapters give a good overview of the approach.

Note added in press: This is an active area of research, with new research papers being published on a monthly basis, such as Chalk et al. (2018)[28] and Liu et al. (2018)[73].

Tutorial Material

Byrne, JH, *Neuroscience Online*, McGovern Medical School University of Texas. http://neuroscience.uth.tmc.edu/index.htm.

Frisby, JP and Stone, JV (2010). *Seeing: The Computational Approach to Biological Vision*. MIT Press.

Laughlin, SB (2006). *The Hungry Eye: Energy, Information and Retinal Function*.
http://www.crsltd.com/guest-talks/crs-guest-lecturers/simon-laughlin.

Lay, DC (1997). *Linear Algebra and its Applications*. Addison-Wesley.

Pierce, JR (1980). *An Introduction to Information Theory: Symbols, Signals and Noise*. Dover Publications.

Riley, KF, Hobson, MP, and Bence, SJ (2006). *Mathematical Methods for Physics and Engineering*. Cambridge University Press.

Scholarpedia. This online encyclopedia includes excellent tutorials on computational neuroscience. www.scholarpedia.org.

Smith, S (1997). *The Scientist and Engineer's Guide to Digital Signal Processing*. Freely available at www.dspguide.com.

Stone, JV (2012). *Vision and Brain: How We See the World*. MIT Press.

Stone, JV (2015). *Information Theory: A Tutorial Introduction*. Sebtel Press.

Appendix A

Glossary

ATP Adenosine triphosphate: molecule responsible for energy transfer.

autocorrelation function Given a sequence $x = (x_1, \ldots, x_n)$, the autocorrelation function specifies how quickly the correlation between nearby values x_i and x_{i+d} diminishes with distance d.

average Given a variable x, the average, mean, or expected value of a sample of n values of x is $\overline{x} = 1/n \sum_{j=1}^{n} x_j$.

bandwidth A signal with frequencies between f_1Hz and f_2Hz has a bandwidth of $W = (f_2 - f_1)$Hz.

binary digit A binary digit can be either a 0 or a 1.

bit The information required to choose between two equally probable alternatives. Often confused with a binary digit (Section 2.2).

central limit theorem As the number of samples from almost any distribution increases, the distribution of sample means becomes increasingly Gaussian.

channel capacity The maximum rate at which a channel can communicate information from its input to its output.

coding capacity The maximum amount of information that could be conveyed by a neuron with a given firing rate.

coding efficiency The proportion ϵ of a neuron's output entropy that provides information about the neuron's input.

conditional probability The probability that the value of one random variable x has the value y_1 given that the value of another random variable y has the value y_1, written as $p(x_1|y_1)$.

conditional entropy Given two random variables x and y, the average uncertainty regarding the value of x when the value of y is known, $H(x|y) = E[\log(1/p(x|y))]$ bits.

convolution A filter can be used to change (blur or sharpen) a signal by convolving the signal with the filter, as defined in Section 6.4.

correlation See Appendix C for correlation and covariance.

covariance matrix Given a vector variable $\mathbf{x} = (x_1, \ldots, x_m)^T$, the $m \times m$ covariance matrix is $\mathbb{C} = E[\mathbf{x}\mathbf{x}^T]$. See page 86.

cross-correlation function Given two sequences $x=(x_1,...,x_n)$ and $y=(y_1,...,y_n)$, the cross-correlation function specifies how quickly the correlation between x_i and y_{i+d} diminishes with abs(d).

cumulative distribution function The integral of (i.e. cumulative area under) the probability density function (pdf) of a variable.

decoding Translating neural outputs (e.g. firing rates) to inputs (e.g. stimulus values).

decorrelated See uncorrelated.

dynamic linearity If a neuron's response to a sinusoidal input is a sinusoidal output then it has dynamic linearity.

efficient coding hypothesis Sensory data is encoded to maximise information rates, subject to physiological constraints on space, time, and energy.

entropy The entropy of a variable y is a measure of its variability. If y adopts m values with independent probabilities $p(y_1),...,p(m)$ then its entropy is $H(y)=\sum_{i=1}^{m} p(y_i)\log_2 1/p(y_i)$ bits.

equiprobable Values that are equally probable are equiprobable.

equivariant Variables that have the same variance are equivariant.

expected value See average.

filter In signal processing, a filter differentially attenuates certain frequencies in the spatial or temporal domain, or both.

Fourier analysis Used to represent (almost) any variable as a weighted sum of sine and cosine functions (see Sections 2.8 and 7.4).

Gaussian variable If the values of a variable x are drawn independently from a Gaussian distribution with a mean μ_x and variance v_x then this is written as $x\sim\mathcal{N}(\mu_x,v_x)$ (Section 2.7).

identity matrix Has 1s on its diagonal elements and 0s elsewhere.

iid If a variable x has values which are sampled independently from the same probability distribution then the values of x are said to be independent and identically distributed (iid).

independence If two variables x and y are independent then the value of x provides no information about the value y, and vice versa.

information The information conveyed by a variable x which adopts the value $x=x_1$ with probability $p(x_1)$ is $\log_2(1/p(x_1))$ bits.

joint probability The probability that two or more variables simultaneously adopt specified values.

Joule One Joule is the energy required to raise 100 g by 1 metre.

kernel See filter.

linear See static linearity and dynamic linearity.

linear decodability If a continuous signal s, which has been encoded as a spike train y, can be reconstructed using a linear filter then it is linearly decodable.

logarithm If $y=\log_a(x)$ (i.e. using logarithms with base a) then y is the power to which a must be raised to obtain x (i.e. $x=a^y$).

mean See average.

metabolic efficiency A neuron that is metabolically efficient encodes sensory data to maximise information transmitted *per Joule*, subject to physiological constraints on information rate, space, and time. Metabolic efficiency is usually defined as the ratio mutual information/energy, but may also refer to entropy/energy.

mitochondrion Cell organelle responsible for generating ATP.

monotonic If y is a monotonic function of x then increasing x always increases y (e.g. $y=x^2$), or always decreases y (e.g. $y=1/x$).

mutual information The reduction in uncertainty $I(y,x)$ regarding the value of one variable x induced by knowing the value of another variable y. Mutual information is symmetric, so $I(y,x)=I(x,y)$.

noise The random 'jitter' that is part of a measured quantity.

natural statistics The statistical distribution of values of a physical parameter (e.g. contrast) observed in the natural world.

orthogonal Perpendicular.

phase The phase of a signal can be considered as its left–right position. A sine and a cosine wave have a phase difference of 90 degrees.

power The rate at which energy is expended per second (Joules/s). The power required for a variable with a mean of zero is proportional to its variance.

power spectrum A graph of frequency versus the power at each frequency for a given signal is the *power spectrum* of that signal.

principal component analysis Given an elliptical cloud of n data points in an m-dimensional space, principal component analysis finds the longest axis of this ellipsoid, $\mathbf{w}_1$, and the second longest, axis $\mathbf{w}_2$ (which is orthogonal to $\mathbf{w}_1$), and so on. Each axis is associated with to one of m *eigenvectors*, and the length of each axis is associated with an *eigenvalue*.

probability distribution Given a variable x which can adopt the values $\{x_1,...,x_n\}$, the probability distribution is $p(x)=\{p(x_1),...,p(x_n)\}$, where $p(x_i)$ is the probability that $x=x_i$.

probability density function (pdf) The probability density function (pdf) $p(x)$ of a continuous random variable x defines the probability density of each value of x. When we wish to refer to a case which includes either continuous or discrete variables, we use the term *probability distribution* in this text.

pyramidal cell Regarded as the computational engine, with various brain regions, in particular the neocortex. Each pyramidal cell receives thousands of synaptic inputs and has an axon which is about 4 cm in length.

random variable (RV) The concept of a random variable x can be understood from a simple example, like the throw of a die. Each physical outcome is a number x_i, which is the value of the random variable, so that $x=x_i$. The probability of each value is defined by a probability distribution $p(x)=\{p(x_1),p(x_2),...\}$.

redundancy Natural signals (e.g. in an image or sound) are redundant, because most values can be predicted from nearby values.

signal In this book, the word signal usually refers to a noiseless variable, whereas the word variable is used to refer to noisy and noiseless variables.

signal-to-noise ratio Given a variable $y=x+\eta$ which is a mixture of a signal x with variance S and noise η with variance N, the signal-to-noise ratio of y is $\mathrm{SNR}=S/N$.

standard deviation The square root σ of the variance of a variable.

static linearity If a system has a static linearity then the response to an input value x_t is proportional to x_t.

theorem A mathematical statement which has been proven to be true.

timing precision If firing rate is measured using a timing interval of $\Delta t=0.001$ s then the timing precision is $\iota=1/\Delta t$ s $= 1,000\mathrm{s}^{-1}$.

transfer function The sigmoidal function $\mathrm{E}[y]=g(x)$ which maps neuronal inputs x to mean output values. Also known as a *static nonlinearity* in signal processing. See encoding function.

tuning function Defines how firing rate changes as a function of a physical parameter, such as luminance, contrast, or colour.

uncertainty In this text, uncertainty refers to the surprisal (i.e. $\log(1/p(y))$) of a variable y.

uncorrelated Variables with a correlation of zero are uncorrelated. See Appendix C.

variable A variable is like a 'container', usually for a number. *Continuous variables* (e.g. temperature) can adopt any value, whereas *discrete variables* (e.g. a die) adopt certain values only.

variance The variance is of x is $\mathrm{var}(x)=\mathrm{E}[(x-\bar{x})^2]$ and is a measure of how 'spread out' the values of a variable are.

vector A vector is an ordered list of m numbers, $\mathbf{x}=(x_1,...,x_m)$.

white Like white light, a signal which contains an equal proportion of all frequencies is white, so it has a flat power spectrum. An iid Gaussian variable (i.e. with uncorrelated values) is white.

Wiener kernel A spatial or temporal filter, which in this text has dynamical linearity.

Appendix B

Mathematical Symbols

$\otimes$ convolution operator. See pages 100 and 122.

Δ (upper case letter delta) represents a small increment.

Δt small timing interval used to measure firing rate.

∇ (nabla, also called del), represents a vector-valued gradient.

$\hat{}$ (hat) used to indicate an estimated value. For example, $\hat{v}_x$ is an estimate of the variance v_x.

$|x|$ indicates the absolute value of x (e.g. if $x=-3$ then $|x|=3$).

$\leq$ less than or equal to.

$\geq$ greater than or equal to.

$\approx$ approximately equal to.

$\sim$ if a random variable x has a distribution $p(x)$ then this is written as $x \sim p(x)$.

$\propto$ proportional to.

A cross-sectional area of an axon. Also 2×2 rotation matrix.

E the mean or *expectation* of the variable x is $E[x]$.

E power, usually measured in pJ/s.

$\sum$ (capital sigma), represents summation. For example, if we represent the $n=3$ numbers 2, 5, and 7 as $x_1=2$, $x_2=5$, $x_3=7$ then their sum x_{sum} is

$$x_{sum} \quad = \quad \sum_{i=1}^{n} x_i = x_1 + x_2 + x_3 = 2 + 5 + 7.$$

The variable i is counted up from 1 to n, and for each i, the term x_i adopts a new value and is added to a running total.

$\prod$ (capital pi) represents multiplication. For example, if we use the values defined above then the product of these $n=3$ integers is

$$x_{prod} = \prod_{i=1}^{n} x_i \tag{B.1}$$

$$= x_1 \times x_2 \times x_3 = 2 \times 5 \times 7 = 70.$$

The variable i is counted up from 1 to n, and for each i, the term x_i adopts a new value and is multiplied by a running total.

ϵ (epsilon) coding efficiency, the proportion of a neuron's output entropy which provides information about the neuron's input.

ε (Latin letter epsilon) metabolic efficiency, the number of bits of information (entropy) or mutual information per Joule of energy.

ι (iota) timing precision, $\iota = 1/\Delta t$ s^{-1}.

λ (lambda) mean and variance of Poisson distribution. Also eigenvalue.

λ_s (lambda) space constant used in exponential decay of membrane voltage, the distance over which voltage decays by 67%.

η (eta) noise in ganglion cell output.

ξ (ksi) noise in photoreceptor output.

μ (mu) the mean of a variable; and $1\,\mu$m $= 1$ micron, or 10^{-6} m.

$\rho(x,y)$ (rho) the correlation between x and y.

σ (sigma) the standard deviation of a distribution.

corr(x,y) the estimated correlation between x and y.

cov(x,y) the estimated covariance between x and y.

C channel capacity, the maximum information that can be transmitted through a channel, usually measured in bits per second (bits/s).

$\mathbb{C}$ $m \times m$ covariance matrix of the output values of m cones.

$\mathbb{C}_t$ $m \times m$ temporal covariance matrix of the output values of m cones.

$\mathbb{C}_s$ $m \times m$ spatial covariance matrix of the output values of m cones.

$\mathbb{C}_\eta$ $m \times m$ covariance matrix of noise values.

e constant, equal to $2.7\,1828\,1828\ldots$.

E the mean, average, or *expected value* of a variable x, written as $\mathrm{E}[x]$.

G neural filter.

g neural encoding function, which transforms a signal $s=(s_1,\ldots,s_k)$ into channel inputs $x=(x_1,\ldots,x_n)$, so $x=g(s)$.

$H(x)$ entropy of x, which is the average Shannon information of the probability distribution $p(x)$ of the random variable x.

$H(x|y)$ conditional entropy of the conditional probability distribution $p(x|y)$. This is the average uncertainty in the value of x after the value of y is observed.

$H(y|x)$ conditional entropy of the conditional probability distribution $p(y|x)$. This is the average uncertainty in the value of y after the value of x is observed.

$H(x,y)$ entropy of the joint probability distribution $p(x,y)$.

$I(x,y)$ mutual information between x and y, average number of bits provided by each value of y about the value of x, and vice versa.

I_{max} estimated upper bound on the mutual information $I(x,y)$ between neuronal input and output.

$\ln x$ natural logarithm (log to the base e) of x.

$\log x$ logarithm of x. Logarithms use base 2 in this text, and base is indicated with a subscript if the base is unclear (e.g. $\log_2 x$).

m number of different possible messages or input values.

M number of bins in a histogram.

N variance of noise.

$\mathcal{N}$ if the values of a variable x are drawn independently from a Gaussian distribution with mean μ_x and variance v_x then x is written as $x \sim \mathcal{N}(\mu_x, v_x)$.

n the number of observations in a data set (e.g. coin flip outcomes).

$p(x)$ the probability distribution of the random variable x.

$p(x_i)$ the probability that the random variable x has the value x_i.

$p(x,y)$ joint probability distribution of the random variables x and y.

Mathematical Symbols

$p(x_i|y_i)$ the conditional probability that $x=x_i$ given that $y=y_i$.

R the entropy of a spike train. Also photoreceptor filter.

R_{min} lower bound on the mutual information $I(x,y)$ between neuronal input and output.

R_{info} upper bound on the mutual information $I(x,y)$ between neuronal input and output.

R_{max} neural coding capacity, the maximum entropy of a spike train at a given firing rate.

S variance of signal s. Also power spectrum of image.

s stimulus variable, $s=(s_1,\ldots,s_n)$.

T transpose operator. See Appendix D.

Δt small interval of time; usually, $\Delta t=0.001\,$s for neurons.

v_x if x has mean μ then the variance of x is $v_x=\sigma_x^2=\mathrm{E}[(\mu-x)^2]$.

w vector of m weights comprising a linear encoding kernel; **w** is usually an estimate of the optimal kernel $\mathbf{w}^*$.

x cone output variable.

x vector variable; $\mathbf{x}_t$ is the value of the vector variable **x** at time t.

X vector variable **x** expressed as an $m \times n$ data matrix.

y neuron output variable (firing rate).

y *model* neuron output variable (firing rate).

$\bar{y}$ mean firing rate.

y vector variable; $\mathbf{y}_t$ is the value of the vector variable **y** at time t.

$\bar{y}_C^*$ mean firing rate that maximises information rate (bits/s).

$\bar{y}_M^*$ mean firing rate that maximises metabolic efficiency (bits/pJ).

z input to ganglion cell.

z input to *model* ganglion cell.

z vector variable; $\mathbf{z}_t$ is the value of the vector variable **z** at time t.

Appendix C

Correlation and Independence

Correlation and Covariance. The similarity between two variables x and y is measured in terms of a quantity called the *correlation*. If x has a value x_t at time t and y has a value y_t at the same time t then the *correlation coefficient* between x and y is defined as

$$\rho(x,y) \quad = \quad \frac{1}{c_{xy}} \mathrm{E}[(x_t - \overline{x})(y_t - \overline{y})], \tag{C.1}$$

where $\overline{x}$ is the average value of x, $\overline{y}$ is the average value of y, and c_{xy} is a constant which ensures that the correlation has a value between -1 and $+1$. Given a sample of n pairs of values, the correlation is estimated as

$$\mathrm{corr}(x,y) \quad = \quad \frac{1}{n c_{xy}} \sum_{t=1}^{n} (x_t - \overline{x})(y_t - \overline{y}). \tag{C.2}$$

We are not usually concerned with the value of the constant c_{xy}, but for completeness it is defined as $c_{xy} = \sqrt{\mathrm{var}(x) \times \mathrm{var}(y)}$, where $\mathrm{var}(x)$ and $\mathrm{var}(y)$ are the variances of x and y, respectively. Variance is a measure of the 'spread' in the values of a variable. For example, the variance in x is estimated as

$$\mathrm{var}(x) \quad = \quad \frac{1}{n} \sum_{t=1}^{n} (x_t - \overline{x})^2. \tag{C.3}$$

In fact, it is conventional to use the un-normalised version of correlation, called the *covariance*, which is estimated as

$$\mathrm{cov}(x,y) \quad = \quad \frac{1}{n} \sum_{t=1}^{n} (x_t - \overline{x})(y_t - \overline{y}). \tag{C.4}$$

Because covariance is proportional to correlation, these terms are often used interchangeably.

It will greatly simplify notation if we assume all variables have a mean of zero. For example, this allows us to express the covariance more succinctly as

$$\text{cov}(x,y) \quad = \quad \frac{1}{n}\sum_{t=1}^{n} x_t \times y_t \qquad\qquad (\text{C.5})$$

$$= \quad E[x_t y_t], \qquad\qquad (\text{C.6})$$

and the correlation as $\text{corr}(x,y)=c_{xy}E[x_t y_t]$.

Decorrelation and Independence. If two variables are independent then the value of one variable provides no information about the corresponding value of the other variable. More precisely, if two variables x and y are independent then their joint distribution $p(x,y)$ is given by the product of the distributions $p(x)$ and $p(y)$:

$$p(x,y) \quad = \quad p(x) \times p(y). \qquad\qquad (\text{C.7})$$

In particular, if two signals are Gaussian and they have a joint Gaussian distribution (as in Figure C.1b) then being uncorrelated means they are also independent.

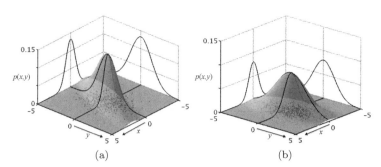

(a)   (b)

Figure C.1. (a) Joint probability density function $p(x,y)$ for correlated Gaussian variables x and y. The probability density $p(x,y)$ is indicated by the density of points on the ground plane at (x,y). The marginal distributions $p(x)$ and $p(y)$ are on the side axes. (b) Joint probability density function $p(x,y)$ for independent Gaussian variables, for which $p(x,y)=p(x)p(y)$.

Appendix D

A Vector–Matrix Tutorial

The single key fact about vectors and matrices is that each vector represents a point located in space, and a matrix moves that point to a different location. Everything else is just details.

Vectors. A number, such as 1.234, is known as a *scalar*, and a *vector* is an ordered list of scalars. Here is an example of a vector with two components a and b: $\mathbf{w} = (a,b)$. Note that vectors are written in bold type. The vector $\mathbf{w}$ can be represented as a single point in a graph, where the location of this point is by convention a distance of a from the origin along the horizontal axis and a distance of b from the origin along the vertical axis.

Adding Vectors. The *vector sum* of two vectors is the addition of their corresponding elements. Consider the addition of two pairs of scalars (x_1, x_2) and (a,b):

$$(a + x_1), \quad (b + x_2). \tag{D.1}$$

Clearly, (x_1, x_2) and (a,b) can be written as vectors:

$$
\begin{aligned}
\mathbf{z} &= (a + x_1), (b + x_2) & \text{(D.2)} \\
&= (x_1, x_2) + (a, b) \\
&= \mathbf{x} + \mathbf{w}. & \text{(D.3)}
\end{aligned}
$$

Thus the sum of two vectors is another vector; it is known as the *resultant* of those two vectors.

Subtracting Vectors. Subtracting vectors is similarly implemented by the subtraction of corresponding elements so that

$$
\begin{aligned}
\mathbf{z} &= \mathbf{x} - \mathbf{w} & \text{(D.4)} \\
&= (x_1 - a), (x_2 - b). & \text{(D.5)}
\end{aligned}
$$

Multiplying Vectors. Consider the sum given by the multiplication of two pairs of scalars, (x_1, x_2) and (a, b):

$$y = ax_1 + bx_2. \tag{D.6}$$

Clearly, (x_1, x_2) and (a, b) can be written as vectors:

$$y = (x_1, x_2).(a, b),$$
$$= \mathbf{x.w}, \tag{D.7}$$

where equation (D.7) is to be interpreted as equation (D.6). This multiplication of corresponding vector elements is known as the *inner, scalar,* or *dot* product, and is often denoted with a dot, as here.

Vector Length. First, as each vector represents a point in space it must have a distance from the origin; this distance is known as the vector's length or *modulus* and is denoted by $|\mathbf{x}|$ for a vector $\mathbf{x}$. For a vector $\mathbf{x} = (x_1, x_2)$ with two components, this distance is given by the length of the hypotenuse of a triangle with sides x_1 and x_2, so that

$$|\mathbf{x}| = \sqrt{x_1^2 + x_2^2}. \tag{D.8}$$

Angle between Vectors. The angle between two vectors $\mathbf{x}$ and $\mathbf{w}$ is

$$\cos\theta = \frac{\mathbf{x.w}}{|\mathbf{x}||\mathbf{w}|}. \tag{D.9}$$

Crucially, if $\theta = 90°$ then the inner product is zero, because $\cos 90 = 0$, irrespective of the lengths of the vectors. Vectors at $90°$ to each other are known as *orthogonal vectors*.

Row and Column Vectors. Vectors come in two basic flavours, *row vectors* and *column vectors*. A simple notational device to transform a row vector (x_1, x_2) into a column vector (or vice versa) is the *transpose operator, T*:

$$(x_1, x_2)^T = \begin{pmatrix} x_1 \\ x_2 \end{pmatrix}. \tag{D.10}$$

The reason for having row and column vectors is because it is often necessary to combine several vectors into a single *matrix* which is then used to multiply a single vector $\mathbf{x}$, defined here as

$$\mathbf{x} = (x_1, x_2)^T. \tag{D.11}$$

In such cases it is necessary to keep track of which vectors are row vectors and which are column vectors. If we redefine $\mathbf{w}$ as a column vector, $\mathbf{w}=(a,b)^T$, then the inner product $\mathbf{w}.\mathbf{x}$ can be written as

$$y \;=\; \mathbf{w}^T\mathbf{x} \tag{D.12}$$

$$\;=\; (a,b)\begin{pmatrix} x_1 \\ x_2 \end{pmatrix} \tag{D.13}$$

$$\;=\; ax_1 + bx_2. \tag{D.14}$$

Here, each element of the row vector $\mathbf{w}^T$ is multiplied by the corresponding element of the column $\mathbf{x}$, and the results are summed. Writing the inner product in this way allows us to specify many pairs of such products as a vector–matrix product.

If $\mathbf{x}$ is a vector variable such that x_1 and x_2 have been measured n times (e.g. at n time consecutive time steps) then y is a variable with n values

$$(y_1,y_2,...,y_n) \;=\; (a,b)\begin{pmatrix} x_{11}, & x_{12}, & ..., & x_{1n} \\ x_{21}, & x_{22}, & ..., & x_{2n} \end{pmatrix}. \tag{D.15}$$

Here, each (single element) column y_{1t} is given by the inner product of the corresponding column in $\mathbf{x}$ with the row vector $\mathbf{w}$. This can now be rewritten succinctly as

$$y \;=\; \mathbf{w}^T\mathbf{x}.$$

Vector–Matrix Multiplication. If we reset the number of times $\mathbf{x}$ has been measured to $N=1$ for now then we can consider the simple case of how two scalar values y_1 and y_2 are given by the inner products

$$y_1 \;=\; \mathbf{w}_1^T\mathbf{x} \tag{D.16}$$

$$y_2 \;=\; \mathbf{w}_2^T\mathbf{x}, \tag{D.17}$$

where $\mathbf{w}_1=(a,b)^T$ and $\mathbf{w}_2=(c,d)^T$. If we consider the pair of values y_1 and y_2 as a vector $\mathbf{y}=(y_1,y_2)^T$ then we can rewrite equations (D.16) and (D.17) as

$$(y_1,y_2)^T \;=\; (\mathbf{w}_1^T\mathbf{x},\mathbf{w}_2^T\mathbf{x})^T. \tag{D.18}$$

If we combine the column vectors $\mathbf{w}_1$ and $\mathbf{w}_2$ then we can define a *matrix* W:

$$W \;=\; (\mathbf{w}_1,\mathbf{w}_2)^T \tag{D.19}$$

$$\;=\; \begin{pmatrix} a & b \\ c & d \end{pmatrix}. \tag{D.20}$$

We can now rewrite equation (D.18) as

$$(y_1, y_2)^T \;=\; \begin{pmatrix} a & b \\ c & d \end{pmatrix}(x_1, x_2)^T. \qquad\qquad (\text{D.21})$$

This can be written more succinctly as $\mathbf{y} = W\mathbf{x}$. This defines the standard syntax for vector–matrix multiplication. Note that the column vector $(x_1, x_2)^T$ is multiplied by the first row in W to obtain y_1 and is multiplied by the second row in W to obtain y_2.

Just as the vector $\mathbf{x}$ represents a point on a plane, so the point $\mathbf{y}$ represents a (usually different) point on the plane. Thus *the matrix W implements a linear geometric transformation of points from $\mathbf{x}$ to $\mathbf{y}$.*

If $n > 1$ then the tth column $(y_{1t}, y_{2t})^T$ in $\mathbf{y}$ is obtained as the product of the tth column $(x_{1t}, x_{2t})^T$ in $\mathbf{x}$ with the row vectors in W:

$$\begin{pmatrix} y_{11}, & y_{12}, & \dots, & y_{1n} \\ y_{21}, & y_{22}, & \dots, & y_{2n} \end{pmatrix} \;=\; \begin{pmatrix} a & b \\ c & d \end{pmatrix} \begin{pmatrix} x_{11}, & x_{12}, & \dots, & x_{1n} \\ x_{21}, & x_{22}, & \dots, & x_{2n} \end{pmatrix}$$

$$= \; (\mathbf{w}_1, \mathbf{w}_2)^T (x_1, x_2)^T \qquad\qquad (\text{D.22})$$

$$= \; W\mathbf{x}. \qquad\qquad (\text{D.23})$$

Each (single element) column in y_1 is a scalar value which is obtained by taking the inner product of the corresponding column in $\mathbf{x}$ with the first row vector $\mathbf{w}_1^T$ in W. Similarly, each column in y_2 is obtained by taking the inner product of the corresponding column in $\mathbf{x}$ with the second row vector $\mathbf{w}_2^T$ in W.

Transpose of Vector–Matrix Product. It is useful to note that if $\mathbf{y} = W\mathbf{x}$ then the transpose $\mathbf{y}^T$ of this vector–matrix product is

$$\mathbf{y}^T = (W\mathbf{x})^T = \mathbf{x}^T W^T, \qquad\qquad (\text{D.24})$$

where the transpose of a matrix is defined by

$$W^T = \begin{pmatrix} a & b \\ c & d \end{pmatrix}^T = \begin{pmatrix} a & c \\ b & d \end{pmatrix}. \qquad\qquad (\text{D.25})$$

Matrix Inverse. By analogy with scalar algebra, if $\mathbf{y} = W\mathbf{x}$ then $\mathbf{x} = W^{-1}\mathbf{y}$, where W^{-1} is the inverse of W. If the columns of a matrix are orthogonal then $W^{-1} = W^T$.

This tutorial is reproduced from Independent Component Analysis (2004) by JV Stone, with permission from MIT Press.

Appendix E

Neural Information Methods

Consider a temporal sequence of stimulus values x and the resultant neuron outputs y, which can be either a sequence of continuous values or a sequence of spikes. The mutual information between x and y is defined as

$$
\begin{aligned}
I(x,y) &= H(y) - H(y|x) & \text{(E.1)} \\
&= H(x) - H(x|y) & \text{(E.2)} \\
&\leq 0.5 \log(1 + SNR) \text{ bits}, & \text{(E.3)}
\end{aligned}
$$

where SNR is the signal-to-noise ratio, with equality if each variable is independent and Gaussian. The mutual information can be estimated using three broad strategies[22], which provide: (1) a direct estimate using Equation E.1, (2) an upper bound using Equation E.3, and (3) a lower bound using Equation E.2. For simplicity, stimulus values (s in the main text) are represented as x here, so that $y = g(x) + \eta$, where g is a neuron transfer function and η is a noise term.

The Direct Method

The total entropy $H(y)$ is essentially a global measure of how much the response sequence varies over time. In contrast, the noise entropy $H(y|x)$ is a measure of how much variation in the response sequence remains after the stimulus value at each point in time has been taken into account. Therefore, the difference between $H(y)$ and $H(y|x)$ is a measure of the amount of variation in the response sequence that can be attributed to the stimulus sequence.

Estimating the Entropy of a Spike Train. In physics, the entropy of a jar of gas is proportional to the volume of the jar. By analogy, we can treat a spike train as if it were a one-dimensional jar, so that spike train entropy is proportional to the amount of time T over which the spike train is measured: $H(T, \Delta t) \propto T$, where Δt defines the temporal resolution used to measure spikes. Dividing $H(T, \Delta t)$ by T yields the *entropy rate*, which converges to the entropy $H(y)$ for large values of T; specifically,

$$H(y) \quad = \quad \lim_{T \to \infty} \frac{H(T, \Delta t)}{T} \quad \text{bits/s.} \tag{E.4}$$

Strong et al. (1998)[118] use arguments from statistical mechanics to show that a graph of $H(T, \Delta t)/T$ versus $1/T$ should yield a straight line (see also Appendix A.8 in Bialek, 2012[18]). The x-intercept of this

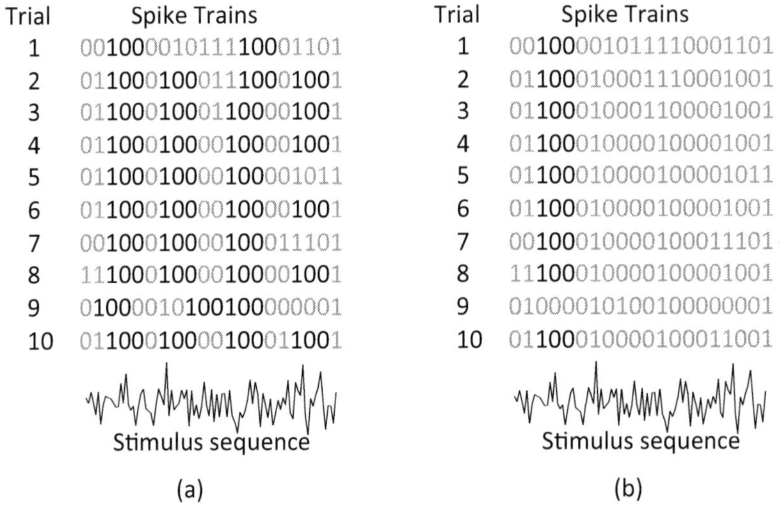

Trial	Spike Trains	Trial	Spike Trains
1	00**100**001011110001101	1	00**100**001011110001101
2	011000**100**01110001001	2	011000**100**01110001001
3	011000**100**01100001001	3	011000**100**01100001001
4	011000**100**00100001001	4	011000**100**00100001001
5	011000**100**00100001011	5	011000**100**00100001011
6	011000**100**00100001001	6	011000**100**00100001001
7	001000**100**00100011101	7	001000**100**00100011101
8	111000**100**00100001001	8	111000**100**00100001001
9	01000010**100**100000001	9	01000010**100**100000001
10	011000**100**00100011001	10	011000**100**00100011001

Stimulus sequence

(a)

Stimulus sequence

(b)

Figure E.1. The direct method (schematic). The same stimulus sequence is repeated for $N=10$ trials and the N response sequences are recorded; a spike is represented as 1 and no spike as 0.

(a) Total entropy $H(y)$ is estimated from the probability of particular spike trains within a long unique spike train sequence (which is the concatenation of 10 trials here). The probability $p(y)$ of a particular T-element spike train y is estimated as the number of instances of y expressed as a proportion of all T-element spike trains. For example, in the data above, there are 170 places where a three-element spike train could occur, and there are 35 instances of the spike sequence $y = [100]$ (marked in bold), so $p(y) = 35/170 \approx 0.206$.

(b) Noise entropy $H(y|x)$ is estimated from the conditional probability of particular spike trains. The same stimulus value occurs at the same time in each of $N=10$ trials. Therefore, the conditional probability $p(y|x)$ of the response y to a stimulus subsequence x which starts at time t is the number N_y of trials which contain y at time t expressed as a proportion of the number N of spike trains that begin at time t (i.e. $p(y|x) = p(y|t)$). For example, there are $N_y = 9$ instances of the spike sequence $y = [100]$ at $t=3$ (marked in bold), so the conditional probability is $p(y = [100]|t=3) = 9/10 = 0.9$.

line is at $1/T = 0$, corresponding to a y-intercept of $H(T,\Delta t)/T$ at $T = \infty$, which is therefore the entropy $H(y)$.

The direct method usually involves two types of output sequences: *unique* and *repeated*. The unique spike train is a response to a long sequence of inputs; this is used to estimate the total spike train entropy. The repeated spike train sequence consists of spike trains obtained in response to N repeats of a stimulus sequence; these are used to estimate the entropy of the noise in the spike train. However, if the repeated sequence is sufficiently long then the entire set of N response sequences can be treated as a unique spike train, as in Figure E.1.

Estimating Total Entropy $H(y)$. The entropy $H(T,\Delta t)$ for one value of T is estimated from the probability $p(y^i)$ of the m_T different observed sequences $y^1,...,y^{m_T}$ of length T:

$$H(T,\Delta t) \quad = \quad \sum_{i=1}^{m_T} p(y^i)\log\frac{1}{p(y^i)}, \tag{E.5}$$

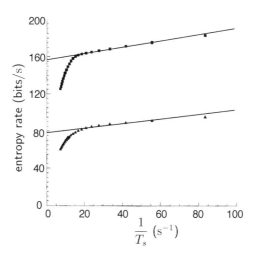

Figure E.2. The direct method. Entropy and noise entropy rates for a visual neuron (H1 in the fly), responding to a randomly moving visual image. The filled circles in the upper trace show the full spike-train entropy rate for different values of $1/T$ (with $\Delta t = 3$ ms). The straight line is an extrapolation to $1/T = 0$ (i.e. $T \to \infty$) and yields $H(y)$. The lower trace shows the spike-train noise entropy rate for different values of $1/T$, and the straight line is again an extrapolation to $1/T = 0$ and yields $H(y|x)$. The difference between the ordinate intercepts of the two straight lines is $H(y) - H(y|x)$ and is therefore the mutual information rate (Equation E.1). Reproduced with permission from Strong et al. (1998)[118].

where $p(y^i)$ is the number of instances of the sequence y^i, expressed as a proportion of the number of different sequences of length T observed anywhere in the unique output sequence (see Figure E.1a).

The entropy of the output sequence is found by estimating $H(T, \Delta t)/T$ for successively larger values of T and then extrapolating to find the entropy at $1/T = 0$ (i.e. at $T = \infty$). In the limit $T \to \infty$,

$$H(y) \quad = \quad \lim_{T \to \infty} \frac{H(T, \Delta t)}{T} \qquad \text{(E.6)}$$

$$= \quad \lim_{T \to \infty} \frac{1}{T} \sum_{i=1}^{m_T} p(y^i) \log \frac{1}{p(y^i)}, \qquad \text{(E.7)}$$

as shown by the upper line in Figure E.2.

Estimating Noise Entropy $H(y|x)$. The stimulus sequence x is repeated N times, so there are a total of N similar response sequences. The conditional (i.e. noise) entropy is estimated as

$$H(y|x) \quad \approx \quad \mathrm{E}_t[H(y|x^t)], \qquad \text{(E.8)}$$

where x^t is the stimulus subsequence starting at time t and y is the corresponding response. Note that this average is taken over successive time indices between $t = 1$ and $t = n - T$. $H(y|x^t)$ is the entropy of the output sequences y^i given x^t (analogous to Equation E.7):

$$H(y|x^t) \quad = \quad \lim_{T \to \infty} \frac{1}{T} \sum_{i=1}^{m_t} p(y^i|x^t) \log \frac{1}{p(y^i|x^t)}, \qquad \text{(E.9)}$$

where $p(y^i|x^t)$ is the number of instances of the sequence y^i expressed as a proportion of the number of different sequences of length T observed at time t in the output sequences (see Figure E.1b). Note that the same stimulus value occurs at the same time in each trial, so $p(y|x^t) = p(y|t)$. As above, $H(y|x^t)$ is found by evaluating the right-hand side of Equation E.9 for successively larger values of T and extrapolating to find the entropy at $1/T = 0$ (i.e. at $T = \infty$), as shown by the lower line in Figure E.2. Finally, mutual information is estimated from Equation E.1. See also Nemenman, Shafee, and Bialek (2002)[81].

Assumptions. Inputs are repeated many times. Data are spike trains. The estimation process makes no assumptions regarding the distribution of variables and therefore requires large amounts of data.

The Upper Bound Method

If the noise η in the output y has an independent Gaussian distribution then the mutual information between x and y is maximised provided x also has an independent Gaussian distribution. Thus, if the input x is Gaussian and independent then the estimated mutual information provides an upper bound. Additionally, if each variable is Gaussian (but not necessarily independent) with a bandwidth of W Hz then its entropy is the sum of the entropies of its Fourier components. To review Fourier analysis, see Sections 2.8 and 7.4.

In common with the direct method, input sequences need to be repeated many times, but the number N of trials (repeats) required here is fewer. This is because a Gaussian distribution is defined in terms of its mean and variance, so, in effect, we only need to estimate a few means and variances from the data.

Estimating Output Signal Power

1. Find the average output sequence $\bar{y} = 1/N \sum_{i=1}^{N} y^i$.
2. Obtain Fourier coefficient $(a(f), b(f))$ of $\bar{y}$ at each frequency f.
3. Estimate the power of each frequency f as $\mathcal{S}(f) = a(f)^2 + b(f)^2$.

Estimating Output Noise Power

1. Estimate the noise $\eta^i = y^i - \bar{y}$ in each of the N output sequences.
2. Find the Fourier coefficient $(a(f), b(f))$ of η^i at each frequency f.
3. Estimate the power at each frequency f as $\mathcal{N}^i(f) = a(f)^2 + b(f)^2$.
4. Find the average power of each Fourier component

$$\mathcal{N}(f) \quad = \quad \frac{1}{N} \sum_{i=1}^{N} \mathcal{N}^i(f). \tag{E.10}$$

Assuming a Nyquist sampling rate of $2W$ Hz, estimate the mutual information $I(x,y)$ by summing over frequencies (as in Equation 2.28):

$$R_{info} \quad = \quad \sum_{f=0}^{W} \log\left(1 + \frac{\mathcal{S}(f)}{\mathcal{N}(f)}\right) \text{ bits/s}, \tag{E.11}$$

where $R_{info} \geq I(x,y)$, with equality if each variable is iid Gaussian.

Assumptions. The response sequences to each of N repeats of the same stimulus sequence are continuous. Each output sequence is Gaussian, but not necessarily independent (iid).

The Lower Bound Method

Unlike previous methods, this method does not rely on repeated presentations of the same stimulus, and it can be used for spiking or continuous outputs. In both cases, we can use the neuron inputs x and outputs y to estimate a linear decoding filter $\mathbf{w}_d$. When the output sequence is convolved with this filter, it provides an estimate $x_{est} = \mathbf{w}_d \otimes y$ of the stimulus x, where $\otimes$ is the convolution operator. We assume that $x = x_{est} + \xi_{est}$, so that the estimated noise in the estimated stimulus sequence is $\xi_{est} = x - x_{est}$ (Figure 1.3).

Assuming a bandwidth of W Hz and that values are transmitted at the Nyquist rate of $2W$ Hz, we Fourier transform the stimulus sequence x to find the signal power $\mathcal{X}(f)$ at each frequency f and Fourier transform ξ_{est} to find the power in the estimated noise $\mathcal{M}(f)$ at each frequency. The mutual information is estimated by summing over frequencies:

$$R_{min} = H(x) - H(\xi_{est}) \tag{E.12}$$

$$= \sum_f \log \mathcal{X}(f) - \sum_f \log \mathcal{M}(f) \tag{E.13}$$

$$= \sum_{f=0}^{W} \log \frac{\mathcal{X}(f)}{\mathcal{M}(f)} \quad \text{bits/s,} \tag{E.14}$$

where $R_{min} \leq I(x,y)$, with equality if each variable is iid Gaussian.

Assumptions. The stimulus sequence x is Gaussian, but not necessarily independent (iid). Outputs are spiking or continuous.

Further Reading. This account is based on Strong et al. (1998)[118], Rieke et al. (1997)[98], Borst and Theunissen (1999)[22], Dayan and Abbot (2001)[33], and Niven et al. (2007)[83]. Relevant developments can be found in Nemenman, Shafee, and Bialek (2002)[81], Juusola et al. (2003, 2016)[57;58], Ince et al. (2009)[53], Goldberg et al. (2009)[48], Crumiller et al. (2013)[31], Valiant and Valiant (2013)[119], and Dettner et al. (2016)[35].

Appendix F

Key Equations

Logarithms use base 2 unless stated otherwise.

Entropy

$$H(s) \;=\; \sum_{i=1}^{m} p(x_i) \log \frac{1}{p(x_i)} \;\; \text{bits} \tag{F.1}$$

$$H(s) \;=\; \int_x p(x) \log \frac{1}{p(x)} \, dx \;\; \text{bits} \tag{F.2}$$

Joint Entropy

$$H(x,y) \;=\; \sum_{i=1}^{m}\sum_{j=1}^{m} p(x_i,y_j) \log \frac{1}{p(x_i,y_j)} \;\; \text{bits} \tag{F.3}$$

$$H(x,y) \;=\; \int_y \int_x p(x,y) \log \frac{1}{p(x,y)} \, dx \, dy \;\; \text{bits} \tag{F.4}$$

$$H(x,y) \;=\; I(x,y) + H(x|y) + H(y|x) \;\; \text{bits} \tag{F.5}$$

Conditional Entropy

$$H(y|s) \;=\; \sum_{i=1}^{m}\sum_{j=1}^{m} p(x_i,y_j) \log \frac{1}{p(x_i|y_j)} \;\; \text{bits} \tag{F.6}$$

$$H(y|x) \;=\; \sum_{i=1}^{m}\sum_{j=1}^{m} p(x_i,y_j) \log \frac{1}{p(y_j|x_i)} \;\; \text{bits} \tag{F.7}$$

$$H(x|y) \;=\; \int_y \int_x p(x,y) \log \frac{1}{p(x|y)} \, dx \, dy \;\; \text{bits} \tag{F.8}$$

$$H(y|x) \;=\; \int_y \int_x p(x,y) \log \frac{1}{p(y|x)} \, dx \, dy \;\; \text{bits} \tag{F.9}$$

$$H(x|y) \;=\; H(x,y) - H(y) \;\; \text{bits} \tag{F.10}$$

$$H(y|x) \;=\; H(x,y) - H(x) \;\; \text{bits,} \tag{F.11}$$

Key Equations

from which we obtain the *chain rule for entropy*:

$$H(x,y) = H(x) + H(y|x) \text{ bits} \tag{F.12}$$
$$= H(y) + H(x|y) \text{ bits} \tag{F.13}$$

Marginalisation

$$p(x_i) = \sum_{j=1}^{m} p(x_i,y_j), \qquad p(y_j) = \sum_{i=1}^{m} p(x_i,y_j) \tag{F.14}$$

$$p(x) = \int_y p(x,y)\,dy, \qquad p(y) = \int_x p(x,y)\,dx \tag{F.15}$$

Mutual Information

$$I(x,y) = \sum_{i=1}^{m}\sum_{j=1}^{m} p(x_i,y_j) \log \frac{p(x_i,y_j)}{p(x_i)p(y_j)} \text{ bits} \tag{F.16}$$

$$I(x,y) = \int_y\int_x p(x,y) \log \frac{p(x,y)}{p(x)p(y)}\,dx\,dy \text{ bits} \tag{F.17}$$

$$I(x,y) = H(x) + H(y) - H(x,y) \tag{F.18}$$
$$= H(x) - H(x|y) \tag{F.19}$$
$$= H(y) - H(y|x) \tag{F.20}$$
$$= H(x,y) - [H(x|y) + H(y|x)] \text{ bits} \tag{F.21}$$

If $y = x + \eta$, with x and y (not necessarily iid) Gaussian variables, then

$$I(x,y) = \int_{f=0}^{W} \log\left(1 + \frac{S(f)}{N(f)}\right) df \text{ bits/s,} \tag{F.22}$$

where W is the bandwidth, $S(f)/N(f)$ is the signal-to-noise ratio of the signal and noise Fourier components at frequency f (Section 2.8), and data are transmitted at the Nyquist rate of $2W$ samples/s.

Channel Capacity

$$C = \max_{p(x)} I(x,y) \text{ bits per value.} \tag{F.23}$$

If the channel input x has variance S, the noise η has variance N, and both x and η are iid Gaussian variables then $I(x,y) = C$, where

$$C = \frac{1}{2}\log\left(1 + \frac{S}{N}\right) \text{ bits per value,} \tag{F.24}$$

where the ratio of variances S/N is the signal-to-noise ratio.

References

[1] Adelson, EH and Bergen, JR. Spatiotemporal energy models for the perception of motion. *J Opt Soc America A*, 2(2):284–299, 1985.

[2] Adrian, ED. The impulses produced by sensory nerve endings: Part I. *J Physiology*, 61:49–72, 1926.

[3] Alexander, RM. *Optima for Animals*. Princeton University Press, 1996.

[4] Atick, JJ. Could information theory provide an ecological theory of sensory processing? *Network: Computation in Neural Systems*, 3(2):213–251, 1992.

[5] Atick, JJ, Li, Z, and Redlich, AN. Understanding retinal color coding from first principles. *Neural Computation*, 4(4):559–572, 1992.

[6] Atick, JJ and Redlich, AN. Towards a theory of early visual processing. *Neural Computation*, 2(3):308–320, 1990.

[7] Atick, JJ and Redlich, AN. What does the retina know about natural scenes? *Neural Computation*, 4(2):196–210, 1992.

[8] Attneave, F. Some informational aspects of visual perception. *Psychological Review*, pages 183–193, 1954.

[9] Attwell, D and Laughlin, SB. An energy budget for signaling in the grey matter of the brain. *J Cerebral Blood Flow and Metabolism*, 21(10):1133–1145, 2001.

[10] Baddeley, R, Abbott, LF, Booth, MCA, Sengpiel, F, Freeman, T, Wakeman, EA, and Rolls, ET. Responses of neurons in primary and inferior temporal visual cortices to natural scenes. *Proc Royal Society London B*, 264:1775–1783, 1997.

[11] Bair, W. *Analysis of Temporal Structure in Spike Trains of Visual Cortical Area MT*. PhD thesis, California Institute of Technology, 1996.

[12] Balasubramanian, V. Heterogeneity and efficiency in the brain. *Proc IEEE*, 103(8):1346–1358, 2015.

[13] Balasubramanian, V and Sterling, P. Receptive fields and functional architecture in the retina. *J Physiology*, 587(12):2753–2767, 2009.

[14] Barlow, HB. Sensory mechanisms, the reduction of redundancy, and intelligence. In Blake, DV and Utlley, AM, editors, *Proc Symp Mechanisation of Thought Processes, Vol 2*. HM Stationery Office, 1959.

[15] Barlow, HB. Possible principles underlying the transformations of sensory messages. *Sensory Communication*, pages 217–234, 1961.

[16] Barlow, HB, Fitzhugh, R, and Kuffler, SW. Change of organization in the receptive fields of the cat's retina during dark adaptation. *J Physiology*, 137:338–354, 1957.

[17] Bell, AJ and Sejnowski, TJ. An information-maximization approach to blind separation and blind deconvolution. *Neural Computation*, 7:1129–1159, 1995.

[18] Bialek, W. *Biophysics: Searching for Principles*. Princeton University Press, 2012.

[19] Bialek, W, DeWeese, M, Rieke, F, and Warland, D. Bits and brains: Information flow in the nervous system. *Physica A: Statistical*

Mechanics and its Applications, 200(1–4):581–593, 1993.

[20] Bogacz, R. A tutorial on the free-energy framework for modelling perception and learning. *J Mathematical Psychology*, 2015.

[21] Borghuis, BG, Ratliff, CP, Smith, RG, Sterling, P, and Balasubramanian, V. Design of a neuronal array. *J Neurosc.*, 28(12):3178–3189, 2008.

[22] Borst, A and Theunissen, FE. Information theory and neural coding. *Nature Neuroscience*, 2(11):947–957, 1999.

[23] Brainard, DH, Longere, P, Delahunt, PB, Freeman, WT, Kraft, JM, and Xiao, B. Bayesian model of human color constancy. *J Vision*, 6(11), 2006.

[24] Brendel, W, Bourdoukan, R, Vertechi, P, Machens, CK, and Denéve, S. Learning to represent signals spike by spike, 2017. arXiv:1703.03777.

[25] Brenner, N, Bialek, W, and de Ruyter van Steveninck, R. Adaptive rescaling maximizes information transmission. *Neuron*, 26:695–702, 2000.

[26] Brenner, N, Strong, SP, Koberle, R, Bialek, W, and de Ruyter van Steveninck, RR. Synergy in a neural code. *Neural Computation*, 12(7):1531–1552, 2000.

[27] Buchsbaum, G and Gottschalk. Trichromacy, opponent colours coding and optimum colour information transmission in the retina. *Proc Royal Society London B*, 220(1218):89–113, 1983.

[28] Chalk, M, Marre, O, and Tkačik, G. Toward a unified theory of efficient, predictive, and sparse coding. *Proc National Academy of Sciences USA*, 115(1):186–191, 2018.

[29] Charnov, EL. Optimal foraging, the marginal value theorem. *Theoretical Population Biology*, 9(2):129–136, 1976.

[30] Cover, TM and Thomas, JA. *Elements of Information Theory*. New York, John Wiley and Sons, 1991.

[31] Crumiller, M, Knight, B, and Kaplan, E. The measurement of information transmitted by a neural population: Promises and challenges. *Entropy*, 15(9):3507–3527, 2013.

[32] Davies, NB, Krebs, JR, and West, SA. *An Introduction to Behavioural Ecology*. Wiley, 2012.

[33] Dayan, P and Abbott, LF. *Theoretical Neuroscience*. MIT Press, New York, NY, USA, 2001.

[34] de Ruyter van Steveninck, RR and Laughlin, SB. The rate of information transfer at graded-potential synapses. *Nature*, 379(6566):642, 1996.

[35] Dettner, A, Münzberg, S, and Tchumatchenko, T. Temporal pairwise spike correlations fully capture single-neuron information. *Nature Communications*, 7, 2016.

[36] DeWeese, MR. *Optimization Principles for the Neural Code*. PhD thesis, Princeton University, 1995.

[37] DeWeese, MR and Bialek, W. Information flow in sensory neurons. *Il Nuovo Cimento D*, 17(7-8):733–741, 1995.

[38] Doi, E, Gauthier, JL, Field, GD, Shlens, J, Sher, A, Greschner, M, Machado, TA, Jepson, LH, Mathieson, K, Gunning, DE, Litke, AM, Paninski, L, Chichilnisky, EJ, and Simoncelli, EP. Efficient coding of spatial information in the primate retina. *J Neuroscience*, 32(46):16256–16264, 2012.

[39] Duffy, KR and Hubel, DH. Receptive field properties of neurons in the primary visual cortex under photopic and scotopic lighting conditions. *Vision Research*, 47:2569–2574, 2007.

[40] Eliasmith, C and Anderson, CH. *Neural Engineering*. MIT Press, 2004.

[41] Fairhall, AL, Lewen, GD, Bialek, W, and de Ruyter van Steveninck, RR. Efficiency and ambiguity in an adaptive neural code. *Nature*, 412(6849):787–792, 2001.

[42] Faisal, AA and Laughlin, SB. Stochastic simulations on the reliability of action potential propagation in thin axons. *PLoS Comp Biol*, 3(5):e79, 2007.

[43] Finelli, LA, Haney, S, Bazhenov, M, Stopfer, M, and Sejnowski, TJ. Synaptic learning rules and sparse coding in a model sensory system. *PLoS Comp Biology*, 4(4), 2008.

[44] Foldiak, P and Young, M. Sparse coding in the primate cortex. In Arbib, MA (ed.), *The Handbook of Brain Theory and Neural Networks*, pages 895–898, 1995.

[45] Frisby, JP and Stone, JV. *Seeing: The Computational Approach to Biological Vision*. MIT Press, 2010.

[46] Gaudry, Kate S and Reinagel, Pamela. Benefits of contrast normalization demonstrated in neurons and model cells. *J Neuroscience*, 27(30):8071–8079, 2007.

[47] Gerstner, W and Kistler, WM. *Spiking Neuron Models: Single Neurons, Populations, Plasticity*. CUP, 2002.

[48] Goldberg, David H, Victor, Jonathan D, Gardner, Esther P, and Gardner, Daniel. Spike train analysis toolkit: enabling wider application of information-theoretic techniques to neurophysiology. *Neuroinformatics*, 7(3):165–178, 2009.

[49] Guo, D, Shamai, S, and Verdú, S. Mutual information and minimum mean-square error in Gaussian channels. *IEEE Transactions on Information Theory*, 51(4):1261–1282, 2005.

[50] Harris, JJ, Jolivet, R, Engl, E, and Attwell, D. Energy-efficient information transfer by visual pathway synapses. *Current Biology*, 25(24):3151–3160, 2015.

[51] Hartline, HK. Visual receptors and retinal interaction, 1967. Nobel Lecture.

[52] Hosoya, T, Baccus, SA, and Meister, M. Dynamic predictive coding by the retina. *Nature*, 436(7047):71–77, 2005.

[53] Ince, RAA, Petersen, RS, Swan, DC, and Panzeri, S. Python for information theoretic analysis of neural data. *Frontiers in Neuroinformatics*, 3, 2009.

[54] Jacobs, A L, Fridman, G, Douglas, RM, Alam, NM, Latham, PE, Prusky, GT, and Nirenberg, S. Ruling out and ruling in neural codes. *Proc National Academy of Sciences USA*, 106(14):5936–5941, 2009.

[55] Jarvstad, A, Rushton, SK, Warren, PA, and Hahn, U. Knowing when to move on cognitive and perceptual decisions in time. *Psychological Science*, 23(6):589–597, 2012.

[56] Johnson, EC, Jones, DL, and Ratnam, R. A minimum-error, energy-constrained neural code is an instantaneous-rate code. *J Computational Neuroscience*, 40(2):193–206, 2016.

[57] Juusola, M, Dau, A, and Lei Z, Diana R. Electrophysiological method for recording intracellular voltage responses of *Drosophila* photoreceptors and interneurons in vivo. *JoVE*, (112), 2016.

[58] Juusola, M and de Polavieja, GG. The rate of information transfer of naturalistic stimulation by graded potentials. *J General Physiology*, 122(2):191–206, 2003.

[59] Koch, K, McLean, J, Berry, M, Sterling, P, Balasubramanian, V, and Freed, MA. Efficiency of information transmission by retinal ganglion

cells. *Current Biology*, 14(17):1523 – 1530, 2004.

[60] Koch, K, McLean, J, Segev, R, Freed, MA, Berry, MJ, Balasubramanian, V, and Sterling, P. How much the eye tells the brain. *Current Biology*, 16(14):1428–1434, 07 2006.

[61] Kostal, L, Lansky, P, and Rospars, J-P. Efficient olfactory coding in the pheromone receptor neuron of a moth. *PLoS Comp Biol*, 4(4), 2008.

[62] Kuffler, SW. Discharge patterns and functional organization of mammalian retina. *J Neurophysiology*, 16:37–68, 1953.

[63] Land, MF and Nilsson, DE. *Animal Eyes*. OUP, 2002.

[64] Laughlin, SB. A simple coding procedure enhances a neuron's information capacity. *Z Naturforsch*, 36c:910–912, 1981.

[65] Laughlin, SB. Matching coding to scenes to enhance efficiency. In Braddick, OJ and Sleigh, AC (eds), *Physical and Biological Processing of Images*, pages 42–52. Springer, Berlin, 1983.

[66] Laughlin, SB. Form and function in retinal processing. *Trends in Neurosciences*, 10:478–483, 1987.

[67] Laughlin, SB, de Ruyter van Steveninck, RR, and Anderson, JC. The metabolic cost of neural information. *Nature Neurosc*, 1(1):36–41, 1998.

[68] Laughlin, SB, Howard, J, and Blakeslee, B. Synaptic limitations to contrast coding in the retina of the blowfly *Calliphora*. *Proc Royal Society London B*, 231(1265):437–467, 1987.

[69] Lennie, P. The cost of cortical computation. *Current Biology*, 13:493–497, 2003.

[70] Levy, WB and Baxter, RA. Energy efficient neural codes. *Neural Computation*, 8(3):531–543, 1996.

[71] Linsker, R. Self-organization in perceptual network. *Computer*, pages 105–117, 1988.

[72] Liu, P and Cheng, B. Limitations of rotational manoeuvrability in insects and hummingbirds: evaluating the effects of neuro-biomechanical delays and muscle mechanical power. *J Royal Society Interface*, 14(132):20170068, 2017.

[73] Liu, Y, Yue, Y, Yu, Y, Liu, L, and Yu, L. Effects of channel blocking on information transmission and energy efficiency in squid giant axons. *J Computational Neuroscience*, 44(2):219–231, 2018.

[74] London, M, Roth, A, Beeren, L, Häusser, M, and Latham, PE. Sensitivity to perturbations in vivo implies high noise and suggests rate coding in cortex. *Nature*, 466(7302):123, 2010.

[75] MacKay, DM and McCulloch, WS. The limiting information capacity of a neuronal link. *Bull. Mathematical Biophysics*, 14(2):127–135, 1952.

[76] Mainen, ZF and Sejnowski, TJ. Reliability of spike timing in neocortical neurons. *Science*, 268(5216):1503, 1995.

[77] Marr, D. *Vision: A Computational Investigation into the Human Representation and Processing of Visual Information*. MIT Press, 2010. Originally published by W.H. Freeman, 1982.

[78] Mather, G. *Foundations of Perception*. Taylor and Francis, 2006.

[79] Meister, M and Berry, MJ. The neural code of the retina. *Neuron*, 22:435–450, 1999.

[80] Moujahid, A, D'Anjou, A, and Graña, M. Energy demands of diverse spiking cells from the neocortex, hippocampus, and thalamus. *Frontiers in Computational Neuroscience*, 8:41, 2014.

[81] Nemenman, I, Shafee, F, and Bialek, W. Entropy and inference, revisited. In Dietterich, TG, Becker, S, and Ghahramani, Z (eds), *Advances in Neural Information Processing Systems 14*. MIT Press,

2002.

[82] Nirenberg, S, Carcieri, SM, Jacobs, AL, and Latham, PE. Retinal ganglion cells act largely as independent encoders. *Nature*, 411(6838):698–701, June 2001.

[83] Niven, JE, Anderson, JC, and Laughlin, SB. Fly photoreceptors demonstrate energy-information trade-offs in neural coding. *PLoS Biology*, 5(4), 03 2007.

[84] Nyquist, H. Certain topics in telegraph transmission theory. *Proc IEEE*, 90(2):280–305, 1928.

[85] Oja, E. Oja learning rule. *Scholarpedia*, 3(3):3612, 2008.

[86] Pajevic, S and Basser, PJ. An optimum principle predicts the distribution of axon diameters in white matter. *PLoS ONE*, 8(1), 2013.

[87] Park, M and Pillow, JW. Bayesian efficient coding, 2017. bioRxiv:178418.

[88] Perge, JA, Koch, K, Miller, R, Sterling, P, and Balasubramanian, V. How the optic nerve allocates space, energy capacity, and information. *J Neuroscience*, 29(24):7917–7928, 2009.

[89] Perge, JA, Niven, JE, Mugnaini, E, Balasubramanian, V, and Sterling, P. Why do axons differ in caliber? *J Neuroscience*, 32(2):626–638, 2012.

[90] Persi, E, Hansel, D, Nowak, L, Barone, P, and van Vreeswijk, C. Power-law input-output transfer functions explain the contrast-response and tuning properties of neurons in visual cortex. *PLoS Comp Biol*, 7(2):e1001078, 02 2011.

[91] Pitkow, X and Meister, M. Decorrelation and efficient coding by retinal ganglion cells. *Nature Neuroscience*, 15(4):628–635, 04 2012.

[92] Plumbley, MD. Efficient information transfer and anti-Hebbian neural networks. *Neural Networks*, 6:823–833, 1993.

[93] Plumbley, MD and Fallside, F. The effect of receptor signal-to-noise levels on optimal filtering in a sensory system. In *Acoustics, Speech, and Signal Processing (ICASSP) 1991*, pages 2321–2324. IEEE, 1991.

[94] Rajan, K and Bialek, W. Maximally informative 'stimulus energies' in the analysis of neural responses to natural signals. *PLoS ONE*, 8(11):e71959, 2013.

[95] Rao, RPN and Ballard, DH. Predictive coding in the visual cortex: a functional interpretation of some extra-classical receptive-field effects. *Nature Neuroscience*, 2:79–87, 1999.

[96] Reza, FM. *Information Theory*. New York, McGraw-Hill, 1961.

[97] Rieke, F, Bodnar, DA, and Bialek, W. Naturalistic stimuli increase the rate and efficiency of information transmission by primary auditory afferents. *Proc Royal Society London B*, 262(1365):259–265, 1995.

[98] Rieke, F, Warland, D, de Ruyter van Steveninck, RR, and Bialek, W. *Spikes: Exploring the Neural Code*. MIT Press, Cambridge, MA, 1997.

[99] Riley, KF, Hobson, MP, and Bence, SJ. *Mathematical Methods for Physics and Engineering*. Cambridge University Press, 2006.

[100] Ruderman DL, Cronin, TW and Chiao, C. Statistics of cone responses to natural images: implications for visual coding. *J Optical Society of America*, 15:2036–2045, 1998.

[101] Saul, AB and Humphrey, AL. Spatial and temporal response properties of lagged and nonlagged cells in cat lateral geniculate nucleus. *J Neurophysiology*, 64(1):206–224, 1990.

[102] Schultz, SR. Signal-to-noise ratio in neuroscience. *Scholarpedia*, 2(6):2046, 2007.

[103] Sengupta, B, Stemmler, MB, and Friston, KJ. Information and efficiency in the nervous system – a synthesis. *PLoS Comp Biol*, 2013.

[104] Shannon, CE. A mathematical theory of communication. *Bell System Technical Journal*, 27:379–423, 1948.

[105] Shannon, CE and Weaver, W. *The Mathematical Theory of Communication*. University of Illinois Press, 1949.

[106] Sharpee, T, Rust, NC, and Bialek, W. Analyzing neural responses to natural signals: maximally informative dimensions. *Neural Computation*, 16(2):223–250, 2004.

[107] Sharpee, TO. Computational identification of receptive fields. *Annual review of neuroscience*, 36:103–120, 2013.

[108] Smith, EC and Lewicki, MS. Efficient auditory coding. *Nature*, 439(7079):978–982, 2006.

[109] Smith, S. *The Scientist and Engineer's Guide to Digital Signal Processing*. 1997. Freely available at www.dspguide.com.

[110] Sokoloff, L. Circulation and energy metabolism of the brain. *Basic Neurochemistry*, 2:338–413, 1989.

[111] Solomon, SG and Lennie, P. The machinery of colour vision. *Nature Reviews Neuroscience*, 8(4):276–286, 2007.

[112] Srinivasan, MV, Laughlin, SB, and Dubs, A. Predictive coding: a fresh view of inhibition in the retina. *Proc Royal Society London B*, 216(1205):427–459, 1982.

[113] Srinivasan, MV, Pinter, RB, and Osorio, D. Matched filtering in the visual system. *Proc Royal Society London B*, 240(1298):279–293, 1990.

[114] Sterling, P and Laughlin, S. *Principles of Neural Design*. MIT Press, 2015.

[115] Stone, JV. *Independent Component Analysis: A Tutorial Introduction*. MIT Press, Boston, 2004.

[116] Stone, JV. *Vision and Brain*. MIT Press, 2012.

[117] Stone, JV. *Information Theory: A Tutorial Introduction*. Sebtel Press, Sheffield, England, 2015.

[118] Strong, SP, Koberle, R, de Ruyter van Steveninck, RR, and Bialek, W. Entropy and information in neural spike trains. *Physical Review Letters*, 80(1):197, 1998.

[119] Valiant, P and Valiant, G. Estimating the unseen: Improved estimators for entropy and other properties. In *Advances in Neural Information Processing Systems*, 2013.

[120] van Hateren, JH. Theoretical predictions of spatiotemporal receptive fields of fly LMCs, and experimental validation. *J Comparative Physiology A*, 171(2):157–170, 1992.

[121] van Hateren, JH. A theory of maximizing sensory information. *Biological Cybernetics*, 68:23–29, 1992.

[122] van Hateren, JH. Processing of natural time series of intensities by the visual system of the blowfly. *Vision Research*, 37(23):3407–3416, 1997.

[123] Vincent, BT and Baddeley, RJ. Synaptic energy efficiency in retinal processing. *Vision Research*, 43(11):1285–1292, 2003.

[124] Vincent, BT, Baddeley, RJ, Troscianko, T and Gilchrist, ID. Is the early visual system optimised to be energy efficient? *Network*, 16, 17–90, 2005.

[125] Wei, X and Stocker, AA. Mutual information, Fisher information, and efficient coding. *Neural Computation*, 28(2):305–326, 2016.

[126] Zhaoping, L. *Understanding Vision: Theory, Models, and Data*. OUP Oxford, 2014.

Index

action potential, 28
adenosine triphosphate (ATP),
    49, 169
aftereffect, 63
apposition eye, 150
autocorrelation function, 106,
    169
automatic gain control, 155
average, 169
axon, 27
axon diameter, 50
    spike speed, 55

bandwidth, 24, 169
binary
    digits vs bits, 11
bit, 10, 12, 169
Bussgang's theorem, 105

calculus of variations, 45, 54
capacity, 17, 169, 190
central limit theorem, 36, 169
channel capacity, 9, 17, 18
chromatic aberration, 64
coding capacity, 33, 43, 58, 169
coding efficiency, 3, 37, 38, 169
colour aftereffect, 63
combination, 35
communication channel, 9
compound eye, 149
conditional entropy, 21, 169
conditional probability, 169
conduction velocity, 28, 55
cone, 64
contrast, 123, 133, 154
convolution operator, 100, 122

cornea, 149
correlation, 169
correlation coefficient, 177
correlation time, 42
covariance, 73, 177
covariance matrix, 86, 107, 169
Cramer-Rao bound, 95
cricket, 39
cross-correlation function, 105,
    109, 170
cumulative distribution func-
    tion, 158, 160, 170

dark noise, 70
data processing inequality, 22
decoding, 170
decorrelated, 170
dendrite, 27
determinant, 86
die, 14
difference-of-Gaussian, 124
differential entropy, 23
direct method, 37, 183
dot product, 76, 100
dynamic linearity, 92, 170
dynamic range, 154

effective noise, 132
efficient coding hypothesis, 4,
    50, 170
efficient metabolic principle,
    165
encoding, 9
entropy, 12, 13, 170, 189
entropy rate, 35, 184
entropy vs information, 15

Dr James Stone is an Honorary Reader in Vision and Computational Neuroscience at the University of Sheffield, England.

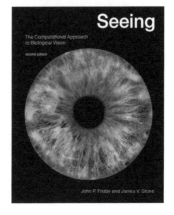

Printed in Great Britain
by Amazon